MOLECULAR FORCES

PETER J. W. DEBYE

MOLECULAR FORCES

BASED ON THE BAKER LECTURES OF

Peter J. W. Debye

BENJAMIN CHU

THE UNIVERSITY OF KANSAS
LAWRENCE, KANSAS

1967

INTERSCIENCE PUBLISHERS
a division of

JOHN WILEY & SONS   NEW YORK · LONDON · SYDNEY

FOREWORD

Forty years ago discussions started about the interpretation of van der Waals' universal molecular attraction as a result of the Coulombic interactions of the electrical components of the molecule. The average electrical field around a molecule was analyzed, which led to its characterization by dipole-, quadrupole-, and higher moments. The mutual orientation effect of such molecules was recognized as a reason for attraction. However, the higher the temperature, the smaller the effect of such an orientation has to become. So the conclusion to be drawn was that at high enough temperatures molecular attraction should vanish. This obviously was in contradiction to the experimental facts, and so the picture of molecules as rigid electrical structures was abandoned. Instead, their structure was recognized as deformable under the influence of an electric field: polarizability was introduced. The result was that, under the combined influence of the electrical field carried by one molecule and the polarization induced by it in its partner an additional potential energy emerges which is proportional to the square of the field and drives the molecules to each other.

This still was not enough, since it made the mutual attraction of single atoms like neon or argon, around which the average field is zero, not understandable. The last difficulty was overcome by London when he recognized that the field important for the interaction should be taken as the instantaneous field. This introduced, unavoidably, quantum theory as a new and essential background, where radiation can no more be derived with confidence from Maxwell's equations.

It was at this juncture that colloid chemistry entered the field with the recognition that the attraction between colloid particles was the result of essentially the same molecular forces as those which determine, for instance, the heat of vaporization of a liquid. Calculations appeared concerning the van der Waals attraction between spheres and plates, giving rise to a series of brilliant experiments, which directly measured van der Waals' forces between plates at distances of the order of the wavelength of visible light, and which also demonstrated that indeed van der Waals' attraction is a result of the electromagnetic interaction of the molecular stray fields.

However, the theory of molecular interaction had first to be refined. The molecular field introduced by London was an electrostatic field. Casimir recognized that its finite velocity of propagation had to be taken account of. One of the most characteristic results of this refinement is the calculation of van der Waals' attraction between two perfect mirrors. This attraction depends solely on two fundamental constants, Planck's quantum of action h and the light velocity c, and illustrates emphatically how intimate the relation is between van der Waals' universal attraction and the quantum fluctuations of the electromagnetic field.

In recent times observations on the critical opalescence have also entered the field as appropriate for the measurement of molecular forces. In the vicinity of the critical point, interactions are observed which are apparently of long-range character extending over distances of the order of the wavelength of visible light. The way this can be understood as a result of long-range correlation, based on short-range interactions, is the main subject of the last chapter.

This is, in short, the story Chu tries to tell. He does it in a way which I personally happen to like very much, emphasizing the physical reasons for what is happening, and reducing the mathematical description to its simplest possible form.

P. J. W. Debye

PREFACE

This book is based on a course of eight Baker lectures on molecular forces recently delivered at Cornell University by Professor Peter J. W. Debye. The style and contents of the lectures have been partially preserved so that readers may enjoy some of the penetrating remarks and insights from one of the great masters in the field.

The subject matter has been kept intelligible to readers without advanced knowledge of mathematics and physics. A sketch on the nature, character, and origin of molecular forces, including applications of such forces to colloid stability and critical opalescence, is presented. I have derived some of the more important equations and hope that this volume may serve not only as an introduction but also as a stimulant providing a renewed interest to the general scientist in the application of molecular forces to problems in chemical physics.

I want to thank Professor Debye, to whom I owe so much in so many respects, for his encouragement, advice, and help in bringing this volume into being; The University of Kansas for a grant to " purchase " this manuscript; and Professor R. J. Bearman, Mrs. G. McConkey, and Dr. M. J. Sparnaay for reading all or parts of the manuscript and for making many helpful suggestions.

Lawrence, Kansas
January 1966

B. Chu

TABLE OF CONTENTS

Foreword   v

Preface   vii

CHAPTER 1   **Van der Waals' Equation, Potential Energies, and Cohesive Energy Density**   1

1–1. Formulation of van der Waals' Equation   2

1–2. Assumptions Underlying van der Waals' Equation   3

1–3. Van der Waals' Isotherms   3

1–4. Critical Phenomena and van der Waals' Constants a and b 6

1–5. Law of Corresponding States   8

1–6. Molecular van der Waals' Constants α and β 8

1–7. Potential Energy between Two Molecules— Introduction of the London Forces   11

1–8. Potential Energy between Two Elementary Charges   13

1–9. Cohesive Energy Density   14

References   15

CHAPTER 2   **Clustering and Fundamentals of the**
            Debye-Hückel Theory   17

            2–1. Clustering   17
            2–2. Fundamentals of the Debye-Hückel Theory   18
                 A. Negligible Ion Diameter   24
                 B. Finite Ion Diameter   25
                 References   26

CHAPTER 3   **Origin of Molecular Forces**   29

            3–1. Molecular Forces and Gravitation   29
            3–2. Molecules as Rigid Electrical Systems   30
            3–3. Polarizable Molecules   32
            3–4. Dynamical Electrical Systems; London–van
                 der Waals' Attraction   36
            3–5. Zero-Point Energy   42
                 A. Stefan-Boltzmann Law (1879)   43
                 B. Radiation Laws of Planck, Rayleigh-Jeans, and Wien   43
                 C. Planck's Formula and Zero-Point Energy   47
                 References   48

CHAPTER 4   **Molecular Interaction and Colloid Chemistry**   49

            4–1. Introduction   49
            4–2. Application of the London–van der Waals
                 Attraction to Colloidal Particles   50
                 A. Attraction between Two Spherical Particles   51
                 B. Attraction between a Flat Surface and a Spherical
                    Particle   52
                 C. Attraction between Two Flat Plates   54
            4–3. Attractions Proportional to $1/r^q$ 55
            4–4. Electrical Repulsion between Particles in
                 Electrolyte Solutions   56
                 A. Repulsion between Two Flat Plates   56
                 B. Repulsion between Two Spherical Particles   60
            4–5. Stability Conditions for Colloids   61
                 A. Stability   61
                 B. Coagulation   65
                 References   70

CHAPTER 5 **Modernization of London's Interaction Theory** 71

5–1. Theory 71
5–2. Experiments on van der Waals' Attraction between Two Plates 77
References 80

CHAPTER 6 **Electromagnetic Scattering** 83

6–1. Particle Scattering 83
    A. Maxwell's Equations 85
    B. Rayleigh Scattering 91
    C. Determination of n from Index of Refraction and Turbidity 94
    D. Interference and Phase Factor 97
    E. Radius of Gyration 101
6–2. Scattering by Medium with Irregular Variation of Dielectric Constant 105
    A. Correlation Function 107
    B. Calculation of Correlation Function from Intensity Distribution 111
6–3. Critical Opalescence of One-Component Systems 113
    A. Free Energy of a van der Waals Gas with Variable Density 121
    B. Molecular Energy in a Medium with Variable Density (including the Effect of Gradients of Fluctuations) 123
    C. Light Scattering (Including the Effect of Gradients of Fluctuations) 126
6–4. Generalized Interaction 130
    A. Free Energy 130
    B. Light Scattering (with Generalized Interaction) 133
6–5. Potential Energy and Free Energy of Two-Component Systems with Constant Composition (without Composition Fluctuations) 134
6–6. Classical Composition Fluctuations 137
6–7. Angular Dissymmetry of Critical Opalescence in Liquid Mixtures 141
6–8. Polymer Solutions 148
    A. General Development 148
    B. Polydispersity of Polymers 150
    C. Extension of the Polymer Coil 152

6–9. Transmission Measurements Near the Critical
        Point   161
        A. General Development   161
        B. Range of Molecular Forces   163
6–10. Small-Angle X-Ray Scattering   166
6–11. Inelastic Scattering   169
        Appendix   169
        References   170

Author Index   173

Subject Index   175

MOLECULAR FORCES

VAN DER WAALS' EQUATION, POTENTIAL ENERGIES, AND COHESIVE ENERGY DENSITY

This book deals with forces between molecules and aims to show how various theories have been developed in the course of time. In addition, we shall describe briefly pertinent experiments, including measurements of forces between two parallel plates at distances of the order of the wavelength of visible light and those of electromagnetic scattering of systems in the neighborhood of their critical points. The topics, from our subjective viewpoint, have been limited mainly to discussions which try to clarify the electromagnetic origin of molecular forces, the need to describe such forces according to the rules of quantum mechanics, and the importance of molecular interactions in chemical physics with due emphasis on the behavior of liquids in the neighborhood of the critical point. It would therefore be appropriate to start our discussions with the van der Waals equation.

1-1. FORMULATION OF VAN DER WAALS' EQUATION

To introduce molecular forces, let us go back to the year 1873, when J. D. van der Waals successfully modified the ideal gas equation:

$$PV = NkT$$

in which P is the pressure, k is the Boltzmann constant (1.38×10^{-16} erg deg^{-1}), T is the absolute temperature, N is the number of molecules in volume V, and $N \equiv N_0$ whenever $V \equiv \overline{V}$ [N_0 is Avogadro's number (6.023×10^{23} mole^{-1}) and $\overline{V}$ is the molar volume]. Van der Waals deduced in his thesis (*1*) the famous equation for an imperfect gas. He considered that molecules are not just mass points but have certain extensions in space and that molecules of all kinds attract each other. It is the attractive forces between even uncharged molecules that is our main interest in this volume.

The van der Waals equation is

$$\left(P + \frac{a}{\overline{V}^2}\right)(\overline{V} - b) = N_0 kT \tag{1-1}$$

where a and b are the van der Waals constants. It provided, for the first time, quantitative information about the forces between molecules. The constant a is related to the attractive forces between the molecules, and b depends upon their effective volume. Equation (1-1) reduces to the ideal gas equation if a and b vanish.

Qualitatively, the van der Waals equation represents the following facts:

1. The ideal gas equation can be corrected for molecules with a finite diameter by reducing the actual volume per mole $\overline{V}$ to a smaller "ideal" molar volume, $\overline{V}_{id} \equiv \overline{V} - b$, where b, which depends on the size of the molecules, is a volume correction factor.

2. The attraction between the molecules can be taken into account by reducing the ideal gas pressure, P_{id}, to a smaller actual pressure, $P \equiv P_{id} - a/\overline{V}^2$, where $a/\overline{V}^2$ is a correction factor for intermolecular attractions. Combining the two effects, we obtain the van der Waals equation

$$\left(P + \frac{a}{\overline{V}^2}\right)(\overline{V} - b) = RT$$

where $R \equiv N_0 k$.

1-2. ASSUMPTIONS UNDERLYING VAN DER WAALS' EQUATION

We have very briefly deduced the van der Waals equation on a qualitative basis. The constants a and b should tell us something about forces between molecules and about their molecular extensions.

Let us first consider the potential energy between two uncharged molecules as they approach each other from a large separation distance. When the two molecules are far apart, they attract each other so that there is a negative potential energy. After a certain distance, they start to repel each other very strongly as they approach. Figure 1-1(a) shows a plot of the potential energy of interaction of an isolated pair of molecules $\varepsilon(r)$ as a function of their separation distance r.

In a van der Waals gas, molecules are considered as incompressible hard spheres, and there are molecular attractions. The attraction increases with diminishing separation distance until the two molecules touch. When they touch, the attractive forces change abruptly into an infinitely strong repulsion, as shown in Fig. 1-1(b). The van der Waals equation does not represent the exact mathematical consequences to be derived from the energy curves of the form shown in Fig. 1-1(a). However, it is, in many ways, a reasonable approximation and is a very useful equation of state for qualitative discussions on molecular forces. For example, the order of magnitude of the molecular forces can certainly be derived from the van der Waals constants a and b. Recent developments improved the details about the forces between molecules, but they have not changed the fundamental aspects.

1-3. VAN DER WAALS' ISOTHERMS

The van der Waals equation may be written in the form

$$P = \frac{RT}{\overline{V} - b} - \frac{a}{\overline{V}^2} \tag{1-2}$$

It is a cubic equation in V. Figure 1-2 (2) shows the van der Waals isotherms.

When (1-2) in the form

$$P = \frac{1}{\overline{V} - b}\left[RT - \frac{a(\overline{V} - b)}{\overline{V}^2}\right]$$

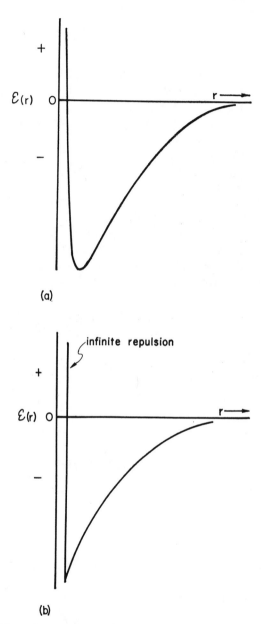

(a)

(b)

Fig. 1-1. (a) Schematic representation of potential energy $\varepsilon(r)$ as a function of separation distance r. (b) Van der Waal's potential energy as a function of separation distance r.

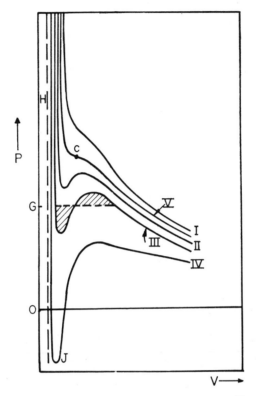

Fig. 1-2. Van der Waals' isothermal curves. $P = [RT/(\overline{V} - b)] - (a/\overline{V}^2)$.

is differentiated with respect to $\overline{V}$ at constant temperature, we get

$$\left(\frac{\partial P}{\partial \overline{V}}\right)_T = -\frac{RT}{(\overline{V} - b)^2} + \frac{2a}{\overline{V}^3} = \frac{-1}{(\overline{V} - b)^2}\left[RT - \frac{2a(\overline{V} - b)^2}{\overline{V}^3}\right] \quad (1\text{-}3)$$

The second differential coefficient is

$$\left(\frac{\partial^2 P}{\partial \overline{V}^2}\right)_T = \frac{2RT}{(\overline{V} - b)^3} - \frac{6a}{\overline{V}^4} = \frac{2}{(\overline{V} - b)^3}\left[RT - \frac{3a(\overline{V} - b)^3}{\overline{V}^4}\right] \quad (1\text{-}4)$$

Let us first consider the isotherms for small values of $\overline{V} - b$ in a P versus V plot. Equation (1-2) tells us that the pressure increases as $1/(\overline{V} - b)$, which means that the pressure increases very strongly with a small decrease in volume when $\overline{V} - b$ is small. Furthermore, for small $\overline{V} - b$, (1-3) suggests that the curve will retain its negative slope, regardless of temperature, as long as the value of $RT - 2a(\overline{V} - b)^2/\overline{V}^3$ remains positive. In the limit as V approaches b, we get a line H, parallel to the P axis, along which the pressure is infinite. This infinite pressure tells us that the molecules in a van der Waals gas are incompressible.

At higher temperatures, as in curve I of Fig. 1-2, $(\partial P/\partial \overline{V})_T$ will always have a negative slope. There only one root of the cubic equation in V is real, the other two being imaginary. As the temperature gets lower and lower, we come to a case where at a point C the isotherm exhibits a horizontal inflection, and the three roots become identical. In Fig. 1-2, isotherm V is at the critical temperature, and point C is the critical point at which both the first and the second derivatives of the pressure with respect to the volume at constant temperature are equal to zero; i.e., $(\partial P/\partial \overline{V})_T = 0$, $(\partial^2 P/\partial \overline{V}^2)_T = 0$. Now if we go to temperatures below the critical temperature, all three values of $\overline{V}$ are real, as shown in Fig. 1-2, curves II and III, where G is the vapor pressure of the saturated vapor for curve III. If we go to still lower temperatures, the van der Waals isotherms cross the V axis. The part below the V axis corresponds to a negative pressure (Fig. 1-2, curve IV). Both the negative pressure and isotherms of the metastable state, as represented by the wiggles in curves III and IV of Fig. 1-2, are queer things.

When we compress a gas at a temperature lower than the critical temperature, the gas begins to condense at a certain pressure. Liquid and gas are on top of each other, and the gas condenses under a constant pressure until only liquid exists. From there on the pressure goes up rather strongly, because we are compressing the liquid. The negative pressure may be taken to represent a metastable state for a liquid, which would be in a state of tension. The point of maximum tension is represented by a minimum in the PV curve (Fig. 1-2, point J).

1-4. CRITICAL PHENOMENA AND VAN DER WAALS' CONSTANTS *a* AND *b*

The critical point (Fig. 1-2, point C) not only corresponds to a certain temperature but also characterizes a definite volume which we define as the *critical volume* and a definite pressure which we call the *critical pressure*. We would expect to learn something about a and b from the observed critical data, so we ask what a and b mean from a molecular point of view.

One thing should shock us already. The critical point is characterized by three known quantities: the critical temperature, the critical pressure, and the critical volume, all of which can be determined experimentally. Yet we have only two unknown constants, a and b. Is there then a relation between the three knowns? In calculating the critical point from van der Waals' equation, we first get the pressure in terms of the variables V and T, then we locate the inflection point by equating $(\partial P/\partial V)_T$ and $(\partial^2 P/\partial V^2)_T$ to zero. From (1-3) and (1-4) it follows that

$$-\frac{RT_c}{(V_c - b)^2} + \frac{2a}{V_c^3} = 0 \quad \text{and} \quad \frac{2RT_c}{(V_c - b)^3} - \frac{6a}{V_c^4} = 0$$

With the original van der Waals equation (1-2) we get V_c, T_c, and P_c in terms of the van der Waals constants a and b:

$$V_c = 3b \qquad T_c = \frac{8a}{27Rb} \qquad P_c = \frac{a}{27b^2} \tag{1-5}$$

If the gas is ideal, $PV/NkT = 1$. According to van der Waals' equation,

$$\frac{P_c V_c}{RT_c} = \frac{3}{8} = 0.375 \tag{1-6}$$

If we know two of these quantities, such as P_c and V_c, we can calculate T_c. This, then, is what van der Waals' equation can predict. As a matter of fact, the term $P_c V_c/N_0 kT_c$ is very nearly a constant for most gases. For example, the critical data for carbon dioxide, which were first investigated by Thomas Andrews many years ago (3), are as follows:

> critical temperature $= T_c = 31.00°C = 304.2°K$
> critical pressure $= P_c = 73.0$ atm
> critical density $= \rho_c = 0.449$ g/ml

Later, in 1937, Michels et al. (4) studied the pressure-volume relations for carbon dioxide at temperatures near the critical temperature and confirmed the above critical data. The critical density for carbon dioxide is about half the density of water. Substituting these observed data, we get $(P_c V_c/RT_c)_{exp} = 0.276$, instead of the theoretical value of 0.375 which we get from van der Waals' equation. A value of 0.28 is fairly close to the actual average value for most of the ordinary gases. It seems that 0.375 and 0.28 are quite different. However, we should bear in mind that we expect only qualitative agreements between the van der Waals equation and experimental data. The fact that the product $(P_c V_c/RT_c)_{exp}$ remains relatively constant is a good sign in itself, even though theoretical and experimental values are not exactly equal.

1-5. LAW OF CORRESPONDING STATES

It is sometimes useful to characterize each gas by its three critical constants, and to express values of pressure, volume, and temperature in terms of reduced variables which are defined as follows†:

$$\pi = \frac{P}{P_c} \qquad \phi = \frac{\overline{V}}{V_c} \qquad \theta = \frac{T}{T_c} \tag{1-7}$$

The constants in the van der Waals equation can also be expressed in terms of the critical constants P_c, V_c, and T_c. With (1-5) we have

$$b = \frac{V_c}{3} \qquad a = 3P_c V_c^2 \qquad R = \frac{8}{3}\frac{P_c V_c}{T_c} \tag{1-8}$$

Substituting (1-7) and (1-8) in the van der Waals equation, we then get the reduced van der Waals equation,

$$\left(\pi + \frac{3}{\phi^2}\right)(3\phi - 1) = 8\theta \tag{1-9}$$

Equation (1-9) is completely general in the realm of the van der Waals equation of state, for it does not involve the molecular constants a and b, and contains no reference to any specific substance. We must, however, remember that the calculation of π, ϕ, and θ requires the values of T_c, P_c, and V_c, which are specific for each substance. With appropriate values of π, ϕ, and θ, the equation should hold for any substance. Substances having the same values of π, ϕ, and θ are said to be in *corresponding states*. The law of corresponding states implies that substances should behave alike when their reduced variables are equal. Equation (1-9) expresses the law of corresponding states for a van der Waals gas and represents only qualitatively the behavior of real gases.

1-6. MOLECULAR VAN DER WAALS' CONSTANTS α AND β

We are finally in a position to estimate the order of magnitude of molecular forces for ordinary gases from the three expressions in (1-8). To bring out the true molecular aspects of a and b, we want to introduce α and β such that $a = N_0^2\alpha$ and $b = N_0\beta$. The van der Waals equation with α and β is

$$P = \frac{nkT}{1 - \beta n} - \alpha n^2 \tag{1-10}$$

† The symbols π, ϕ, and θ were recommended by the Committee on Symbols, *Trans. Faraday Soc.*, **5**, 252 (1910).

where $n = N/V$. From the first two laws of thermodynamics, we know that there is a connection between the thermal equation of state, representing P as a function of V and T, and the caloric equation of state, representing the internal energy U as a function of V and T. For a van der Waals gas,

$$\left(\frac{\partial \bar{U}}{\partial \bar{V}}\right)_T = \frac{a}{V^2}$$

Therefore, integrating at constant temperature, we find for the internal energy per mole,

$$\bar{U} = \text{constant} - \frac{a}{V^2} \qquad \text{or} \qquad \bar{U} = \Theta(T) - nN_0\alpha \qquad (1\text{-}11)$$

as shown in Fig. 1-3.

The caloric equation of state tells us that we have to put in energy in order to take molecules farther apart. This, of course, means that there is an attractive force between the molecules. The values of the constants a and b depend on the nature of the gas. We now substitute $a = N_0^2\alpha$ and $b = N_0\beta$ in the equations $V_c = 3b$, $P_c = (1/27)(a/b^2)$, and $T_c = (8/27)(a/bN_0k)$. Then we get

$$n_c = \frac{1}{3}\frac{1}{\beta} \qquad P_c = \frac{1}{27}\frac{\alpha}{\beta^2} \qquad kT_c = \frac{8}{27}\frac{\alpha}{\beta} \qquad (1\text{-}12)$$

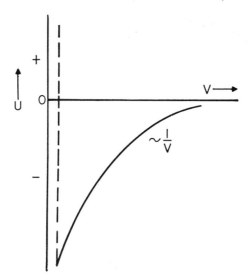

Fig. 1-3. Internal energy U as a function of volume V (according to van der Waals' equation) at constant temperature.

where n_c is the critical-number density and the subscript c indicates values at the critical point. So, if we have measured the critical density, we know β already, and α can be determined by measuring one of the remaining two critical constants. The practical choice is always to determine P_c and T_c, because n_c is much more difficult to measure. We have thus demonstrated that α and β can be calculated from the critical constants.

What do α and β mean? The constant β must be related to the volume of the molecules. The van der Waals equation may take the form

$$P + \frac{\alpha}{v^2} = \frac{kT}{v - \beta}$$

where $v = V/N$. In expanding $[1 - (\beta/v)]^{-1}$ to the first power of β/v, we get

$$P + \frac{\alpha}{v^2} \simeq \frac{kT}{v}\left(1 + \frac{\beta}{v}\right)$$

which reduces to $Pv = kT[1 + (\beta/v)]$ for $\alpha = 0$. With the help of statistical thermodynamics,†

$$\beta = \frac{1}{2}\int_0^\infty (1 - e^{-\varepsilon(r)/kT})4\pi r^2 \, dr$$

For a rigid sphere of diameter $2a$ with no attraction between the molecules,

$$\varepsilon(r) = \begin{cases} +\infty & \text{when } r < 2a \\ 0 & \text{when } r > 2a \end{cases}$$

So,

$$\beta = 4(\tfrac{4}{3}\pi a^3) = 4\omega \tag{1-13}$$

where $\omega\,(= \tfrac{4}{3}\pi a^3)$ is the volume of the rigid sphere.

We now know the significance of β, but what is α? The constant α is related to the attractive forces between the molecules. To consider α in a semiquantitative way, we want to know the potential energy U, in a certain volume V. If we assume that the interaction between two molecules depends only on the distance between their centers, and that the number of molecules per cubic centimeter, n, is a constant, we can say that the potential energy E of one molecule due to surrounding molecules of the same kind is

$$E = \int_d^\infty \varepsilon(r)n \, d\tau = nW \tag{1-14}$$

in which $\varepsilon(r)$ is the potential energy of interaction between two molecules,

† T. L. Hill, *Introduction to Statistical Thermodynamics*, Addison-Wesley, Reading, Mass., 1960.

d is the distance of their closest approach, $d\tau$ ($= 4\pi r^2\, dr$) is a volume element, and the number of molecules in $d\tau$ is given by $n4\pi r^2\, dr$. The quantity $W\left[= \int_d^\infty \varepsilon(r)\, d\tau\right]$ has the dimension of energy times volume.

We can also obtain the total potential energy U_{pot} due to N molecules in volume V,

$$U_{\text{pot}} = \frac{NnW}{2} \tag{1-15}$$

The $\frac{1}{2}$ appears because we have counted each molecule twice—once as a central molecule and once as a surrounding molecule. According to the caloric equation of state, (1-11), van der Waals' α is nothing other than $-W/2$, the volume integral of the energy between two molecules divided by 2. Although we cannot directly obtain the potential energy $\varepsilon(r)$ between two molecules, we do have a volume integral of the energy.

1-7. POTENTIAL ENERGY BETWEEN TWO MOLECULES— INTRODUCTION OF THE LONDON FORCES

The ratio α/β is given by the critical temperature. Since α has the dimensions of energy times volume, and β is a volume, we are going to expect that α/β will really tell us something about the energy. However, we cannot get exact values of the potential energy unless we know a little more about the nature of the potential-energy function $\varepsilon(r)$. London was the first person who really explained how the uncharged molecules attract each other. A force exists even between molecules of the type helium and argon. The London forces (5) are such that the potential energy between two molecules is proportional to the reciprocal sixth power of their separation distance. Let ε_0 be the potential energy between two molecules when they touch each other. It follows that

$$\varepsilon(r) = -\varepsilon_0 \left(\frac{d}{r}\right)^6$$

where d is the diameter of the molecule. $\varepsilon = -\varepsilon_0$ when $r = d$. Then

$$E = n \int \varepsilon(r)\, d\tau$$

$$= -4n\pi\varepsilon_0 \int_{r=d}^{r=\infty} \left(\frac{d}{r}\right)^6 r^2\, dr$$

$$= -\left(\frac{4\pi}{3}\right) n\varepsilon_0 d^3$$

Since ω is the volume of a single molecule and is equal to $(\pi/6)d^3$,

$$E = -8n\omega\varepsilon_0 \tag{1-16}$$

Hence

$$W = -8\omega\varepsilon_0 \quad \text{or} \quad \alpha = \frac{-W}{2} = 4\omega\varepsilon_0 \tag{1-17}$$

Remembering that $\beta = 4\omega$, we finally get

$$\varepsilon_0 = \frac{\alpha}{\beta} \tag{1-18}$$

The quantities ε_0 and ω can be expressed in terms of critical constants from van der Waal's equation:

$$\varepsilon_0 = \frac{27}{8} kT_c \tag{1-19}$$

$$\omega = \frac{1}{32} \frac{kT_c}{P_c} = \frac{1}{12} \frac{1}{n_c} \tag{1-20}$$

As illustrations we shall make numerical calculations for two gases, carbon dioxide and helium. For carbon dioxide, the critical temperature is 304.2°K at a critical pressure of 73.0 atm, whereas helium has a critical temperature of 5.2°K at a critical pressure of 2.26 atm (6). Now with these critical values, we can calculate the volume of a molecule and ε_0, i.e., the value of the potential energy when the two molecules touch each other. Substituting the measured values in (1-19) and (1-20), we obtain d and ε_0, as shown in Table 1-1.

Is the magnitude of ε_0 big or small? Let us compare it with the thermal energy. At ordinary room temperatures, T is approximately 300°K, and hence $kT = 300 \times 1.38 \times 10^{-16} \simeq 4.1 \times 10^{-14}$ erg. According to the law of equipartition, the thermal translational energy of a gas molecule is $\frac{3}{2}kT$,

TABLE 1-1

Determination of Molecular Size and ε_0 from the Critical Constants

	T_c, °K	P_c, atm	α, erg-A^3	β, A^3	d, A	ε_0, ergs
CO_2	304	73.0	9.9×10^{-12}	70.9	3.24	14×10^{-14}
He	5.2	2.26	9.5×10^{-14}	39.2	2.66	0.24×10^{-14}

which is equal to about 6.2×10^{-14} erg. So we see that the potential energy between two CO_2 molecules, even when they touch each other, is only about twice the average kinetic translational energy of one molecule. Hence the CO_2 molecules do not stick to each other very well. In other words, they are not tightly held together. This is why carbon dioxide is a gas at ordinary room temperatures.

In the case of helium, although the values for both T_c and P_c are small, the volume of the molecule ω is proportional to T_c/P_c and is calculated to be 9.85 A^3. The corresponding diameter of a helium molecule is 2.66 A, which is not very much smaller than 3.24 A, the diameter of a carbon dioxide molecule. On the other hand, ε_0 for helium is equal to only 0.24×10^{-14} erg, which means, of course, that the molecules have to go to very low temperatures before they stick together. We see that the energy in this case is quite small. But in the case of ordinary molecules, ε_0 is of the order of magnitude of a few times the thermal translational energy of molecules at room temperature.

1-8. POTENTIAL ENERGY BETWEEN TWO ELEMENTARY CHARGES

We are going to suppose for the present that molecular forces are purely electrostatic in nature and can be derived from Coulomb's law. From this viewpoint, it will be interesting to consider the potential energy of two elementary charges when they are at a distance d apart, and compare it with the potential energy between two uncharged molecules. Let us take $d = 3$ A, and put two electrons at a distance d apart. According to Coulomb's law, the potential energy is e^2/d, and since the charge on an electron is 4.8×10^{-10} esu, we have $e^2/d = 7.68 \times 10^{-12}$ erg $\gg 0.14 \times 10^{-12}$ erg. Therefore, if we took two single elementary charges and placed them at a separation distance equivalent to the molecular dimensions, we would have a much bigger potential energy between two elementary charges than the potential energy between two uncharged molecules. However, we have calculated the potential energy between two elementary charges in vacuum. If we put these elementary charges in a medium, then, of course, we can make the potential energy much lower. The potential energy between two charges in a medium is $e^2/\epsilon d$, where ϵ is the dielectric constant of the medium. For example, if the two charges are in water, the electrical interaction energy between them will be about $(800 \times 10^{-14})/80 = 10 \times 10^{-14}$ erg. This energy has about the same order of magnitude as the potential energy between two uncharged molecules. Although the causes for attraction between ions in water and between uncharged molecules are fundamentally the same, i.e., all these forces are electrical in nature, it may be noted that interactions between uncharged molecules, which consist of a large number of electrons and nuclei, are much more difficult to handle.

1-9. COHESIVE ENERGY DENSITY

Suppose we evaporate 1 cc of benzene. Most of the required energy is being used in taking the molecules away from each other, and in bringing them farther apart. The cohesive energy density (abbreviated CED) roughly corresponds to the amount of work required to change 1 cc of molecules from liquid to gas. The heat of vaporization is, except for a few small corrections, proportional to the potential energy, $-U_{pot}$, as defined in (1-15). By substituting $\alpha = -W/2$ in (1-15) we get

$$-\frac{U_{pot}}{V} = n^2 \alpha$$

The quantity $-U_{pot}/V$, which is the same as the additional pressure due to molecular attraction in the van der Waals equation, is defined as the cohesive energy density. Hildebrand and Scott (7) expressed cohesive energy densities in calories per cubic centimeter and showed that they vary from about 9 cal/cc to about 100 cal/cc. They actually talked about characteristic constants for liquids, and identified these constants as the square roots of the cohesive energy densities.

So as soon as we know the number of molecules per cubic centimeter, n, and the heat of vaporization, we know our ε_0 (or α). For example, let us calculate ε_0 for benzene and for carbon tetrachloride. We shall assume that the volume per molecule ω is approximately equal to d^3 instead of $(\pi/6)d^3$. By definition,

$$W = \int \varepsilon(r)\, d\tau$$

$$= -4\pi\varepsilon_0 \int_d^\infty \left(\frac{d}{r}\right)^6 r^2\, dr$$

$$= -\frac{4\pi}{3} d^3 \varepsilon_0$$

$$\simeq -\frac{4\pi}{3} \frac{\varepsilon_0}{n}$$

or

$$\varepsilon_0 = -\frac{3}{4\pi} nW$$

Since $d_{C_6H_6} = 5.39$ A and $d_{CCl_4} = 5.54$ A, we finally get the results given in Table 1-2. Again, ε_0 has a value which is of the same order of magnitude as that derived for CO_2 from the critical constants.

TABLE 1-2

Determination of Molecular Size and ε_0 from Heat of Vaporization

Sample	Heat of vaporization, cal/g	Temp., °C	Density of liquid, g/cc	CED, cal/cc	$-W$, erg-A^3	ε_0, ergs
C_6H_6	94.3	80.2	0.814	76.8	1.63×10^{-10}	24.4×10^{-14}
CCl_4	46.4	76.7	1.482	68.8	1.71×10^{-10}	23.7×10^{-14}

REFERENCES

1. J. D. van der Waals, Dissertation, Univ. Leiden, 1873; English transl. by J. D. van der Waals, *Physical Memoirs*, Physical Society of London, Vol. I, Pt. 3, Taylor and Francis, London, 1890.

2. J. R. Partington, *An Advanced Treatise on Physical Chemistry*, Vol. I, Longmans, Green, London, 1949, p. 670.

3. T. Andrews, *Phil. Trans. Roy. Soc. London*, **159**, 575 (1869); **166**, 421 (1876); **178**, 45 (1887); *Proc. Roy. Soc. (London)*, **23**, 514 (1875); *J. Chem. Soc. (London)*, **23**, 74 (1870). Through Partington (*2*), p. 624.

4. A. Michels, B. Blaisse, and C. Michels, *Proc. Roy. Soc. (London)*, **A160**, 367 (1937).

5. F. London, *Z. Physik*, **63**, 245 (1930); *Trans. Faraday Soc.*, **33**, 8 (1937); *Z. Phys. Chem.*, **B11**, 222 (1930).

6. H. K. Onnes, *Compt. Rend.*, **147**, 421 (1908); *Koninkl. Ned. Akad. Wetenschap. Proc.*, **12**, 175 (1909).

7. J. H. Hildebrand and R. L. Scott, *The Solubility of Nonelectrolytes*, 3rd ed., Reinhold, New York, 1950; and *Regular Solutions*, Prentice-Hall, Englewood Cliffs, N.J., 1962.

CHAPTER **2**

CLUSTERING AND
FUNDAMENTALS OF
THE DEBYE-HÜCKEL THEORY

2-1. CLUSTERING

We have thus far assumed that molecules are distributed in space in a constant way, and this assumption takes care of the molecular effects from an approximate point of view. Suppose we take a look at gas molecules in a large container. From the outside, the gas molecules seem evenly distributed. They are in a medium of constant average density. Another way of looking at the same thing is to take a *fixed* volume element $d\tau$ inside the container. In that case, the number of molecules in $d\tau$ is constant when averaged over a long time. But if we " sit " on one of those molecules, move with this molecule, and look at the surroundings, we see that the molecule attracts other molecules which are nearby, and so the average density is greater in our immediate neighborhood. This is the "clustering" which was omitted from the van der Waals theory. A theory that neglects clustering sometimes leads to serious errors. For example, clustering has to be taken into account in electrolyte solutions. We now want to show what

17

"clustering" means and when the constant-density assumption is a good approximation.

Clustering becomes an essential effect when the forces between molecules are exerted over large distances, i.e., when there are long-range forces. The longest range force we can have is between charges. The potential energy between two elementary charges is inversely proportional to their separation distance r. If we want to do something about mixtures of charged particles, then we need the volume integral of the potential energy,

$$W = \int_d^\infty \varepsilon(r) \, d\tau \qquad (1\text{-}14)$$

where d is the distance of their closest approach. If $\varepsilon(r)$ is proportional to $1/r$, and $d\tau = 4\pi r^2 \, dr$, then W is proportional to $\int_d^\infty 4\pi r \, dr$, which is infinite! W diverges, and this does not make sense. Here it becomes essential to include clustering, although it does not give us any direct information about the molecular forces themselves.

The forces between charges obey ordinary Coulomb's law. At the same time, let us remember that there is a fundamental energy, kT. The quantity $\frac{3}{2}kT$ is the thermal translational energy of any kind of particle, independent of size and molecular structure. kT is of the order of 4×10^{-14} erg at room temperatures and is very much less at liquid-helium temperatures. We are going to compare all the energies in our discussions with this fundamental energy kT.

How are we going to tackle the problem of clustering? Let us, for example, take the case of ions in an aqueous solution of a strong electrolyte, since the order of magnitude of electrostatic interactions between ions in a dielectric medium, such as water, is comparable to molecular interactions of uncharged molecules. The main question is: If we are in the neighborhood of one of those charges, what is the arrangement of the other charges around this charge? So we have again to "sit" on one of those charges and then ask how the other charges are distributed.

2-2. FUNDAMENTALS OF THE DEBYE-HÜCKEL THEORY

If we sit on a potassium ion in an aqueous solution of potassium chloride, and then look at the surroundings, we see that the chloride ions are attracted and the potassium ions repelled. There are more negative ions in the immediate neighborhood than there are positive ions. In other words, there is a negative ionic atmosphere surrounding the central potassium ion under consideration. The main thing is to know the extension of this atmosphere which can be characterized by a certain length. If we plot the density of these charges versus the distance from the central potassium ion, as in Fig. 2-1, we get a qualitative picture of local densities of negative charges in the neighborhood of a positively charged ion. The density of negative charges falls off to zero at large distances. The effect of the potassium ion is being reduced by the effect of the negative charges around it. If we go far away, then the central potassium ion, surrounded by an atmosphere of negative charges, acts as if the positive ion and its negative ionic atmosphere have a zero charge density. The effect on the surroundings will depend on how far out this compensating atmosphere extends. So we see that there is a certain length which characterizes this ionic atmosphere. The characteristic length is important because it determines the potential energy of the central ion against its surroundings. A solution of this problem is the outcome of the Debye-Hückel theory (*1*).

We are going to discuss the theory very briefly with due emphasis on the nature of clustering involved in the calculation. However, before we plunge into the details of our method, we should make a distinction between theoretical physicists (or chemists) and mathematical physicists (or chemists). A mathematical physicist is very much interested in the mathematical handling of the equations which represent the problem. He is not so much interested in setting up the equations. A theoretical physicist

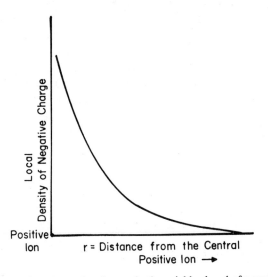

Fig. 2-1. Local density of negative charges in the neighborhood of a positively charged ion.

is very much interested in setting up the equations, and not so much interested in handling the mathematical details of the solutions. Both approaches are inadequate by themselves. We should try to achieve a mean between the two extremes.

One method is to start with the right formulation of the problem, and to keep in mind that it is not always necessary to solve the mathematical equations exactly. It is possible to think of some tricks which we have in our minds because of physical or chemical intuition, and to make good reasonable approximations so that we may get solutions analogous to the van der Waals theory. These solutions are good enough for the understanding of things, but not good enough to predict exact quantitative results. The Debye-Hückel theory is analogous in some respects to van der Waals' generalization of the ideal gas law. However, it has to resort to different expedients, because the electrostatic forces between ions are proportional to $1/r^2$, whereas the intermolecular forces decline much more rapidly with an increase in distance, even though both forces are electrical in nature.

Now let us compute the electric energy of an aqueous solution of a uni-univalent strong electrolyte. If we consider any one ion in an ionic solution, we find that there are, on the average, more dissimilar than similar ions in its surroundings. Suppose in a volume V that there are N molecules of a uni-univalent salt, e.g., potassium chloride, dissociated into ions. Sitting on one of the ions, say a positive potassium ion, we want to ascertain its potential energy with respect to the surrounding ions.

At a point P in the surroundings of the specified ion, there is an electrostatic potential ϕ. This potential ϕ really fluctuates all the time, because the surrounding charges move around. However, we are going to handle this potential as if it were an average of the electrostatic potential generated by the surrounding ions. Poisson's equation tells us how we can calculate this electrostatic potential ϕ:

$$\nabla^2 \phi = -\frac{4\pi\rho}{\epsilon} \tag{2-1}$$

in which ϵ is the dielectric constant of the medium; ∇^2 is the Laplacian operator, $= (\partial^2/\partial x^2) + (\partial^2/\partial y^2) + (\partial^2/\partial z^2)$ in cartesian coordinates; and ρ is the charge density. Both ϕ and ρ are functions of the space coordinates.

If we know the density of charge distribution, we can calculate the electrostatic potential. By definition, the charge density is

$$\rho = n_1 e z_1 + n_2 e z_2 + \cdots = \sum n_i e z_i \tag{2-2}$$

in which n_i is the number of ions per cubic centimeter of the ith kind, e ($= 4.8 \times 10^{-10}$ esu) is the unit electronic charge, and z_i is the number of charges carried by the ith ion, i.e., its valence. The integers $z_1, z_2, \ldots, z_i$ may assume positive as well as negative values. Now, the question is: What is n_i? We know the average value of n_i from concentration measurements; yet on the basis of Ostwald's law (2), we get incorrect results when we use the average value of n_i in calculating osmotic pressure or freezing point of solutions of strong electrolytes. Since the potential energy between such uni-univalent ions corresponds to an energy which is higher than kT, we have to think of the fact that, if we have a certain distribution of charges around a central ion, the thermal energy is not sufficient to produce random motion in all the surrounding ions. This is the clustering problem which we shall consider.

Let us begin by saying that we have an accumulation of negative charges in the neighborhood of a positive central ion. The effect of electrical forces is counteracted by the thermal motion of the ions. To take the thermal motion into account, we implicitly assume that according to the Boltzmann principle, the average charge density of the surrounding ions at a given point can be calculated from the average value of the electrostatic potential at the same point. Boltzmann's law then reduces to

$$n_i = n_i^0 \exp(-z_i e\phi/kT) \tag{2-3}$$

in which n_i^0 is the number of ions per cubic centimeter of the ith kind far from the central ion where $\phi = 0$, and is equal to N/V for uni-univalent electrolytes. Remember that the symbol N is defined as the total number of molecules in a volume V. The situation is analogous to what we see when we think of the atmosphere surrounding the earth. The atmosphere is denser near the surface of the earth than it is higher up. We can calculate what the potential energy of a molecule is at a given height and find that the number of molecules per cubic centimeter at that height is proportional to $\exp(-\text{potential energy}/kT)$. In the present problem we have an electrostatic potential ϕ; the quantity $z_i e\phi$ is the amount of work expended in transporting an ion of the ith kind from infinity to point P. The value of ϕ at point P can be determined as a solution of the equation

$$\nabla^2 \phi = -4\left(\frac{\pi e}{\epsilon}\right) \sum_i n_i^0 z_i \exp(-z_i e\phi/kT) \tag{2-4}$$

We shall introduce the restriction of considering only uni-univalent electrolytes, so that $|z_i| = 1$. Now, $e\phi$ is the work expended in transporting a positive ion from far away to the volume element $d\tau$, where the electrostatic potential is ϕ; and $-e\phi$ is the work expended in moving a negative ion to the same volume element. Since the total charge is equal to zero, $\sum_i N_i z_i = 0$ must hold, where N_i is the total number of ions of the ith kind. From (2-2) and (2-3) we find the charge density:

$$\rho = n^0 e[\exp(-e\phi/kT) - \exp(e\phi/kT)]$$

or

$$\rho = 2n^0 e \sinh(e\phi/kT) \dagger$$

(2-5)

where n^0 is the number of positive (or negative) ions per cubic centimeter far from the central ion where $\phi = 0$. The farther we go from the specified ion, the smaller will be the potential ϕ. If the electrostatic potential is so small that $e\phi/kT$ is much smaller than 1, we can approximate $\exp(e\phi/kT)$ as $1 + e\phi/kT + \cdots$,‡ and get

$$\rho = -\frac{2n^0 e^2 \phi}{kT}$$

(2-6)

Thus a linear relation exists between ρ and ϕ for small ϕ. When ρ from (2-6) is introduced, (2-4) assumes the much simpler form

$$\nabla^2 \phi = \frac{8\pi n^0 e^2 \phi}{\epsilon kT} = \kappa^2 \phi$$

(2-7)

with $\kappa^2 = 8\pi n^0 e^2/\epsilon kT$. The quantity κ^2 has the dimension of the reciprocal of the square of a length. Equation (2-7) is the well-known starting point in the Debye-Hückel theory for strong electrolytes.

It is important to understand the limit of this approximation. For instance, the potential energy involved in bringing a charge to a distance of 5 A from another fixed charge is

$$\frac{e^2}{\epsilon r} = \frac{(4.8 \times 10^{-10})^2}{5 \times 10^{-8} \times 80} \simeq 6 \times 10^{-14} \text{ erg}$$

We remember that kT is approximately 4×10^{-14} erg at ordinary room temperature, and so at a distance of about 5 A this potential energy is of the same order as kT. That is why we have to be careful when we assume $e\phi/kT \ll 1$. In plasmas, $\epsilon = 1$. So the corresponding potential energy would be approximately 80 times more than kT. There the clustering will be very much more pronounced and the differential equation (2-7)

---

† $\sinh x = (e^x - e^{-x})/2$.

‡ $e^x = 1 + x + \cdots$.

becomes a very poor approximation. In fact, it is necessary to go back to fundamentals, although the mathematical difficulties are often very great.

If we only want to get an inkling of what is going on, we can think of a case in which the potential energy is smaller than the thermal energy. We recall that the potential due to thermal motion, ϕ_{kT} $(= kT/e)$, is equal to about 25 mv, whereas the potential due to an elementary charge at a distance of 5 A away is $e/\epsilon r = 36$ mv. Therefore, we can replace $\exp(-e\phi/kT)$ by $1 - e\phi/kT$ only at large distances.

The characteristic length λ $(= 1/\kappa)$ is the distance over which an ion acts in shielding itself:

$$\lambda = \frac{1}{\kappa} = \left(\frac{\epsilon kT}{8\pi n^0 e^2}\right)^{1/2} \propto (C)^{-1/2}$$

where the concentration C is usually expressed in moles per liter of solution. The characteristic length comes out to be about 100 A for a millimolar aqueous solution of a uni-univalent electrolyte, such as sodium chloride or potassium chloride.

We shall now investigate the physical interpretation of our characteristic length λ. In the one-dimensional case, ϕ is only a function of the normal coordinate x, and $\nabla^2\phi$ may be replaced by $d^2\phi/dx^2$. The boundary conditions are $\phi = \phi_0$ for $x = 0$ and tends to zero for large values of x. When $e\phi/kT \ll 1$,

$$\frac{d^2\phi}{dx^2} = \kappa^2\phi \qquad (2\text{-}8)$$

A function which satisfies (2-8) is $\phi = \phi_0 e^{-\kappa x}$. Since $d^2\phi/dx^2$ is also equal to $-4\pi\rho/\epsilon$, the charge density ρ corresponding to the given potential is

$$\rho = -\frac{\epsilon\kappa^2}{4\pi}\phi_0 e^{-\kappa x}$$

The quantity $1/\kappa$, or λ, is a measure of the thickness of the ionic atmosphere. For $\kappa x = 1$, $\phi = \phi_0/e$. At that point λ measures the length within which the charge density of the ionic atmosphere reduces to $1/e$ fraction of its value at $x = 0$. Recall that the exponential $e \simeq 2.72$.

Having clarified the significance of $1/\kappa$, we shall now determine the electrostatic potential and charge density in the neighborhood of a central ion with charge $+e$. The field is spherically symmetrical. Equation (2-7) then becomes

$$\frac{1}{r^2}\frac{d}{dr}\left(r^2\frac{d\phi}{dr}\right) = \kappa^2\phi$$

which has a general solution

$$\phi = A \frac{e^{-\kappa r}}{r} + A' \frac{e^{\kappa r}}{r}$$

Since ϕ approaches 0 as r tends toward infinity, A' can be set equal to zero. The constant A can be determined by using appropriate boundary conditions. Two cases, negligible ion diameter and finite ion diameter, will be discussed.

A. Negligible Ion Diameter

ϕ should approach ϕ_1 when r approaches zero. Consequently,

$$\phi = A \frac{e^{-\kappa r}}{r} = \frac{A}{r}(1 - \kappa r + \tfrac{1}{2}\kappa^2 r^2 - \cdots) \simeq \frac{e}{\epsilon r}$$

for very small r. This gives $A = e/\epsilon$, and we obtain $\phi = (e/\epsilon r)\exp(-\kappa r)$ as the electrostatic potential at a distance r from an ion of charge e in an ionic solution. The potential ϕ is the sum of the potential due to the charge on the ion itself, ϕ_1, and the potential due to the charge of the ion's ionic atmosphere, ϕ_2. So, $\phi_2 = \phi - \phi_1 = (e/\epsilon r)(e^{-\kappa r} - 1)$. For small values of r,

$$\phi_2 \simeq \frac{e}{\epsilon r}(1 - \kappa r) - \frac{e}{\epsilon r} = \frac{-e\kappa}{\epsilon}$$

This potential always has the sign opposite that of the charge on the selected ion, and is the potential due to an ion's ionic atmosphere at the location of the selected ion. The potential energy u of the central ion with respect to its surroundings amounts to

$$u = -\frac{e^2 \kappa}{\epsilon} \tag{2-9}$$

Now, there are N molecules in a volume V dissociating into N positive ions and N negative ions. Each positive ion has a potential difference $-e\kappa/\epsilon$ and each negative ion has a potential difference $e\kappa/\epsilon$ against its surroundings. Then the mutual potential energy of the ionic solution is

$$U_{\text{pot}} = \frac{N}{2} e\left(\frac{-e\kappa}{\epsilon}\right) + \frac{N}{2}(-e)\left(\frac{e\kappa}{\epsilon}\right) = \frac{-Ne^2\kappa}{\epsilon} \tag{2-10}$$

Since $\kappa^2 = 8\pi n^0 e^2/\epsilon kT$, the potential energy is proportional to the square root of the concentration.

B. Finite Ion Diameter

We shall assume that our ions are rigid spheres of diameter d. The interior of each ion has a dielectric constant ϵ and a point charge ($+$ or $-e$) in the center. The magnitude d signifies the minimum distance to which the surrounding ions, negative as well as positive, can approach the singled-out ion.

The boundary conditions for (2-7) are

1. $\phi = 0$ and $d\phi/dr = 0$ for $r = \infty$, whereby we have

$$\phi = (A/r)\exp(-\kappa r)$$

2. $\phi = \phi_d$ for $r = d$. Therefore,

$$\phi_d = \frac{A}{d} e^{-\kappa d} \qquad \text{or} \qquad A = d\phi_d e^{\kappa d}$$

With this evaluation of A we get

$$\phi = \phi_d \frac{d}{r} e^{\kappa(d-r)}$$

Differentiating ϕ with respect to r, we find

$$\frac{d\phi}{dr} = -\phi_d\, de^{\kappa d}(1 + \kappa r)e^{-\kappa r}/r^2$$

For $r = d$, the field strength as well as the potential must be continuous. It follows that

$$\left(\frac{d\phi}{dr}\right)_{r=d} = -\frac{e}{\epsilon d^2} = -\phi_d \frac{1 + \kappa d}{d}$$

or

$$\phi_d = \frac{e}{d\epsilon}\left(\frac{1}{1 + \kappa d}\right) = \frac{e}{d\epsilon}\left(1 - \frac{\kappa d}{1 + \kappa d}\right)$$

Hence

$$\phi = \frac{e}{\epsilon r}\frac{e^{\kappa(d-r)}}{1 + \kappa d} = \frac{e}{\epsilon r} e^{\kappa(d-r)}\left(1 - \frac{\kappa d}{1 + \kappa d}\right) \tag{2-11}$$

The potential ϕ_2 generated by the ionic atmosphere at the center of the selected ion is

$$\phi_2 = \phi_d - \frac{e}{d\epsilon} = -\frac{e\kappa}{\epsilon(1 + \kappa d)}$$

Therefore, the potential energy of a positive ion with respect to the surroundings is

$$u = -\frac{e^2 \kappa}{\epsilon} \frac{1}{1 + \kappa d} \tag{2-12}$$

Comparing (2-12) with (2-9), we see that the size effect of the ion is expressed by a factor of $1/(1 + \kappa d)$.

We have included clustering in calculating the mutual potential energy of the ionic solution. What happens if we try to obtain this potential energy when the ions are assumed to be evenly distributed? It appears as if this energy could be estimated in the following manner: For simplicity, consider the same uni-univalent strong electrolytes with N molecules in volume V, so that there are N ions with charge $+e$ and an equal number of N ions with charge $-e$. The potential energy between two dissimilar ions in a medium of dielectric constant ϵ and at a distance r is $-e^2/\epsilon r$. This distance r may be imagined as the average distance between the ions, and since the volume associated with one ion is equal to $V/2N$, we get $r = (V/2N)^{1/3}$. Thus the mutual potential energy of the ionic solution is

$$U_{\text{pot}} = -\frac{Ne^2}{\epsilon} \left(\frac{2N}{V}\right)^{1/3} \tag{2-13}$$

provided the ions are evenly distributed. Here the potential energy is proportional to the cube root of concentration. This is incorrect, and the calculations made by Ghosh (*3*), based on the cube root of concentration, are to be rejected.

Thus far we have demonstrated that clustering must be considered in calculating the potential energy of ionic solutions. The remaining parts of the theory have been discussed in many books (*4, 5*). We shall leave the details to the interested reader. The fundamentals of the Debye-Hückel theory have served to show that clustering can become very important in certain cases. However, we shall neglect clustering in most of the things we are going to discuss since we are mainly interested in a qualitative understanding of the forces of interaction between uncharged molecules.

REFERENCES

1. P. Debye and E. Hückel, *Physik. Z.*, **24**, 185, 305 (1923); P. Debye, *Physik. Z.*, **25**, 97 (1924).

2. W. Ostwald, *Z. Phys. Chem.*, **2**, 36, 270 (1888); **3**, 170 (1889).

3. J. C. Ghosh, *J. Chem. Soc.* (*London*), **113**, 449, 627, 707, 790 (1918); *Z. Phys. Chem.*, **98**, 211 (1921).

4. R. H. Fowler and E. A. Guggenheim, *Statistical Thermodynamics*, Cambridge Univ. Press, New York, 1956.
5. M. Dole, *Introduction to Statistical Thermodynamics*, Prentice-Hall, Englewood Cliffs, N.J., 1954.

CHAPTER 3

ORIGIN OF
MOLECULAR FORCES

3-1. MOLECULAR FORCES AND GRAVITATION

Before 1920 some people thought that the van der Waals forces might have something to do with gravitation.† However, this is not true, because gravitation is a long-range force (like electrostatic forces, which also are proportional to $1/r^2$), whereas molecular forces are short-range forces (such as London forces, which are proportional to $1/r^7$). To show that molecular forces cannot come from gravitation, we are again going to consider the molecular forces between uncharged particles. As an example, let us take the interactions between two carbon dioxide molecules.

According to the law of equipartition, the thermal translational energy of particles at room temperature is about 6×10^{-14} erg. The potential energy between two carbon dioxide molecules when they touch each other, $-\varepsilon_0$, has a magnitude of 14.0×10^{-14} erg. This is about twice the thermal translational energy. The gravitational energy, $-\varepsilon_0^*$, has a magnitude of $(Gm^2/r)_{r=d}$, in which the constant of gravitation G is 6.67×10^{-8}, provided that m is the mass in grams and r is the distance between the two masses in

† Newton himself probably had an intuitive understanding that molecular forces could not have come from gravitation, since he distinguished the active principles leading to gravitation and cohesion. He also suggested $f = a/r^n$, where f is a force, a is a constant, and the integer $n = 2$ in the case of gravitation. See Newton's *Principia*, a revision of Motte's translation by F. Cajori (University of California Press, 1947), Book I, Section 13, p. 214; and Newton's *Opticks*, 1717, Query 31.

centimeters. The weight of a carbon dioxide molecule is the molecular weight in grams divided by Avogadro's number, and the diameter of a carbon dioxide molecule is about 3.24 A; therefore, the gravitational energy between two CO_2 molecules when they touch each other is

$$-\varepsilon_0^* = -\frac{[(44/6.02) \times 10^{-23}]^2 \times 6.67 \times 10^{-8}}{3.24 \times 10^{-8}} = -1.1 \times 10^{-44} \text{ erg}$$

Since $-\varepsilon_0 = -14.0 \times 10^{-14}$ erg, there is a tremendous factor of 10^{-30} when we compare the magnitude of the molecular interaction energy with that of the gravitational energy. Therefore, gravitation certainly has nothing to do with molecular forces. On the other hand, the gravitational force of attraction is proportional to $1/r^2$, whereas the molecular force of attraction, according to the London theory, is proportional to $1/r^7$. If the particles are far enough apart, gravitational forces can become greater than molecular forces. In fact, at a distance of about $\frac{1}{2}$ mm, we have $\varepsilon = \varepsilon^*$. In other words, if we put one carbon dioxide molecule $\frac{1}{2}$ mm from another carbon dioxide molecule, the molecular forces would be equal to the gravitational forces; and at even larger distances the gravitational forces would be greater.

If molecular forces do not come from gravitation, then what is the nature of these forces? Let us first construct an over-all picture and look at the ideas behind it without going into calculations. We shall then fill this picture with some calculations to show what is right and where the important points are.

3-2. MOLECULES AS RIGID ELECTRICAL SYSTEMS

The first theoretical attempt to explain molecular attraction was set forth in 1912 by W. H. Keesom, who started from a picture of the molecules as a rigid assembly of charges with no resultant net charge (permanent dipoles). The reasoning went like this: All molecules or atoms are electrical systems, and so it follows that molecular forces must be electrical in nature. If every molecule is an assembly of positive and negative charges, it will have an electric field depending on the distribution of the charges in the molecule. If we look at the center of gravity of the positive charges and the center of gravity of the negative charges, we find that some molecules have dipoles, others have quadrupoles. For such molecules, there are lines of force going from the positive to the negative charges. Therefore, dipoles and quadrupoles have electric fields around themselves.

Let us, for example, consider the interaction between dipoles. When a dipole is in the neighborhood of a fixed dipole, the potential energy between them depends on the orientation. If the dipoles are parallel to each other, both positive and negative charges repel, and so there is a repulsive energy, as shown in Fig. 3-1(a). If one of the dipoles is turned around, there is an attractive energy, as shown in Fig. 3-1(b). However, if the second dipole assumes all orientations with respect to the fixed dipole, then, on the average, the potential energy of the second dipole with respect to the fixed dipole is zero. We can reach this conclusion without calculations. Qualitatively we see that, by taking into account all orientations, the charges in the molecule are going to create, on the average, a surface of a sphere with a constant charge density. A sphere with a surface of constant charge density acts as if all the charges were concentrated at the center. If all the

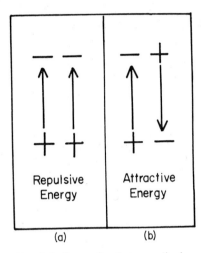

Fig. 3-1. Interaction between dipoles.

charges were at the center, the average field would be zero, because the molecule as a whole is uncharged. However, an effect which orientates the molecules exists, since we could expect no preference in mutual orientation only if the kinetic energy of rotation were infinitely large, i.e., if $T = \infty$. At any finite temperature, orientation with negative potential energy would be preferred. In this way we could have attractions, but the attractions would decrease with increasing temperature and should vanish at infinite temperatures. This model implies that if there is no preferred orientation of the molecules with respect to one another, we shall not have any molecular forces. Such a conclusion on the origin of molecular forces is contradictory to experimental findings because molecular forces exist even in the absence of permanent dipoles.

3-3. POLARIZABLE MOLECULES

The next reasonable explanation appeared around 1920. Since molecular forces exist even for nonpolar molecules, we shall characterize a molecule not only by its dipole, but by the fact that it is deformable. In other words, when we put a molecule in an electric field, the positive charges and the negative charges of the molecule are pushed further apart; i.e., the molecule is polarized. The resultant strain is evidenced as an induced electric moment μ. Actually this induced polarization, α, is only part of the picture: If the molecule has a permanent dipole moment, then the molecule, like an electric magnet, will want to orient itself parallel to the field. If we disregard the permanent moment, the center of positive charges and that of negative charges of an ordinary (nonpolar) molecule coincide in the absence of an electric field.

The induced moment is measurable in terms of the dielectric constant ϵ, with

$$\epsilon - 1 = 4\pi n\alpha \tag{3-1}$$

where n is the number of molecules per cubic centimeter. The induced dipole moment is proportional to the applied electric field $\mathbf{F}$, and the proportionality factor is α; i.e., $\mu = \alpha\mathbf{F}$. In general, α is a tensor. The situation becomes much simpler if α is isotropic. Then the directions of μ and $\mathbf{F}$ coincide and α may be considered as a scalar. The polarizability of a molecule may be defined as the moment the molecule would take in an applied electric field of unity. If we know what the polarizability is, then we know what the dielectric constant is, or vice versa, provided the number of molecules per cubic centimeter is known. Polarizability has the dimension of a volume and is expressible in cubic angstroms. As a matter of fact, the polarizability of a molecule is approximately the same as the average volume of the molecule, and is of the order of a few cubic angstroms. With Maxwell's relation, $\epsilon = \varkappa^2$, in which $\varkappa$ is the index of refraction of the medium, (3-1) changes to

$$\varkappa^2 - 1 = 4\pi n\alpha \tag{3-2}$$

With this equation, we can get the polarizability of most gaseous molecules quite easily.

Now we shall proceed to find the energy of polarization from two different approaches. Suppose that a polarizable molecule is placed in an electric field. Some work is involved in separating the negative and positive charges of the molecule; an additional force exists because the negative and positive charges are some distance away from each other. And if we move this polarized molecule in the field, there is additional work. The energy of polarization E_p is the amount of work involved in bringing a polarizable molecule (or atom) from infinity to a certain point where the electrical field is **F**:

$$E_p = -\int_0^\mu F\,d\mu$$

Since $\mu = \alpha \mathbf{F}$, we have

$$E_p = -\int_0^F \alpha F\,dF = -\tfrac{1}{2}\alpha F^2 \tag{3-3}$$

Equation (3-3) could be deduced from another approach, which gives us additional insight to the forces of attraction between induced dipoles, although the derivation is somewhat cumbersome. It goes as follows. A negative charge, $-e$, in an electric field **F**, has three components of force, $-eF_x$, $-eF_y$, and $-eF_z$, where F_x, F_y, and F_z are, respectively, the x, y, and z components of the electric field in rectangular coordinates. Now if we put a positive charge e at some small distance (ξ, η, ζ) from the center $(0, 0, 0)$, where the negative charge is located, then we have a dipole (Fig. 3-2).

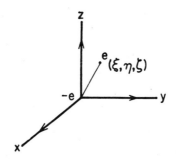

Fig. 3-2. Coordinate system for a dipole.

Such a dipole characterizes a polarizable molecule under the influence of an electric field. To calculate the total force of the dipole, let us look first at the x component of the force. On the negative charge, the force is still $-eF_x$. On the positive charge, we have charge $+e$ times the x component of the field, not at $(0, 0, 0)$, but at (ξ, η, ζ). So we have approximately

$$e\left(F_x + \xi\,\frac{\partial F_x}{\partial x} + \eta\,\frac{\partial F_x}{\partial y} + \zeta\,\frac{\partial F_x}{\partial z} \right)$$

Therefore the total net force in the x direction, $\mathscr{F}_x$, is

$$\mathscr{F}_x = e\xi \frac{\partial F_x}{\partial x} + e\eta \frac{\partial F_x}{\partial y} + e\zeta \frac{\partial F_x}{\partial z}$$

$$= \mu_x \frac{\partial F_x}{\partial x} + \mu_y \frac{\partial F_x}{\partial y} + \mu_z \frac{\partial F_x}{\partial z} \qquad (3\text{-}4)$$

in which $\mu_x = e\xi$, $\mu_y = e\eta$, and $\mu_z = e\zeta$. In an electrostatic field, curl $\mathbf{F} = 0$. Hence

$$\frac{\partial F_x}{\partial y} = \frac{\partial F_y}{\partial x} \qquad \frac{\partial F_x}{\partial z} = \frac{\partial F_z}{\partial x} \qquad (3\text{-}5)$$

Substituting (3-5) in (3-4), we get

$$\mathscr{F}_x = \mu_x \frac{\partial F_x}{\partial x} + \mu_y \frac{\partial F_y}{\partial x} + \mu_z \frac{\partial F_z}{\partial x}$$

Since the induced dipole moment $\boldsymbol{\mu} = \alpha\mathbf{F}$, we have $\mu_x = \alpha F_x$, $\mu_y = \alpha F_y$, and $\mu_z = \alpha F_z$. Thus

$$\mathscr{F}_x = \alpha\left(F_x \frac{\partial F_x}{\partial x} + F_y \frac{\partial F_y}{\partial x} + F_z \frac{\partial F_z}{\partial x} \right)$$

$$= \frac{\alpha}{2} \frac{\partial}{\partial x} (F_x^2 + F_y^2 + F_z^2)$$

$$= \frac{\alpha}{2} \frac{\partial}{\partial x} (F^2)$$

Similarly,

$$\mathscr{F}_y = \frac{\alpha}{2} \frac{\partial}{\partial y} (F^2) \qquad \text{and} \qquad \mathscr{F}_z = \frac{\alpha}{2} \frac{\partial}{\partial z} (F^2)$$

Therefore,

$$E_p = -\tfrac{1}{2}\alpha F^2$$

Polarizability offers an explanation for molecular forces. Since every molecule is surrounded by an electric field, work is gained when we bring other molecules into this electric field. We may argue that rotational motions of the dipole produce a time-dependent electric field which is equal to zero on averaging over all orientations. But the potential energy of polarization, E_p, will not be zero in any case, because E_p is proportional to F^2 and the average of F^2 is always positive (*1*). So we see that there is an energy which is independent of orientation. This potential energy was used by Faraday in his treatment of the magnetic case, and enabled him to make the distinction between paramagnetic and diamagnetic materials.

It is interesting to see how strong such electric fields must be in order to explain the actually observed molecular attraction. For example, as a gas at 1 atm pressure and 0°C, carbon dioxide has an index of refraction of 1.000445 for the sodium D line ($\lambda_0 = 5890$ A). It follows, according to (3-2), that $\alpha = 2.62$ A^3. Assuming now that the polarization energy is equivalent to the van der Waals attraction energy and that nothing else is involved, we find F in the center of one of the two CO_2 molecules when they are touching by equating αF^2 to the value of ε_0 in Table 1-1:

$$\alpha F^2 = \varepsilon_0 \qquad (3\text{-}6)$$

Thus

$$F^2_{CO_2} = \frac{14.0 \times 10^{-14}}{2.62 \times 10^{-24}} = 5.34 \times 10^{10} \text{ (esu)}^2$$

or $F_{CO_2} = 2.31 \times 10^5$ esu $= 69.3 \times 10^6$ volts/cm. In the same way, we find from the index of refraction for He, which is 1.000036, that $\alpha = 0.21$ A^3, and $F_{He} = 1.07 \times 10^5$ esu $= 32.1 \times 10^6$ volts/cm. Thus the order of magnitude of these electric fields is about 10^8 volts/cm or 1 volt/A. The same order of magnitude results when we calculate, for instance, the field in liquid benzene to account for its cohesive energy density. We do this by first calculating the polarizability α from the Lorentz-Lorenz expression:

$$\frac{\varkappa^2 - 1}{\varkappa^2 + 2} \frac{M}{\rho} = \frac{4\pi}{3} N_0 \alpha$$

in which $\varkappa = $ index of refraction $= 1.463$, $M = $ gram molecular weight $= 78.11$ g, $\rho = $ density of liquid $= 0.814$ g/cc, and $N_0 = $ Avogadro's number $= 6.02 \times 10^{23}$ mole^{-1}. Thus $\alpha = 10.4 \times 10^{-24}$ cc. Substituting the values of α and ε_0 (Table 1-2) in (3-6), we get

$$F_{C_6H_6} = 1.53 \times 10^5 \text{ esu} = 45.9 \times 10^6 \text{ volts/cm}$$

We can therefore say that the commonly observed heats of vaporization correspond to the effect of electrical fields of a strength of roughly $\frac{1}{2}$ volt/A. These field strengths are small compared with fields encountered in the interior of atoms. The field acting on an electron in a hydrogen atom in Bohr's first orbit is 60 volts/A.

The explanation based on polarizability is still not quite good enough, because it cannot explain the liquefaction of monatomic rare gases. For example, consider a helium, an argon, or a neon atom. Here the average distribution of the electronic charge around the nucleus has spherical symmetry. On the average, the center of gravity of the positive charges coincides with that of the electrons. According to this point of view, neon, argon, or helium could not be liquefied, because there would be no molecular attraction. This is contradictory to experimental facts. Thus polarizability alone cannot explain the origin of molecular forces.

3-4. DYNAMICAL ELECTRICAL SYSTEMS; LONDON–VAN DER WAALS' ATTRACTION

In 1923 London reasoned that although the average field of a nonpolar molecule is zero, the uncharged molecule must have an instantaneous field. Suppose we take a look at a hydrogen atom with one nucleus and one electron: At each instant, the electron and the positively charged nucleus act like a dipole. Consequently, a field having lines of force going from the positive to the negative charge must exist instantaneously.

In the 1920s it was not quite clear whether or not this instantaneous field should be considered as real. According to Maxwell's electromagnetic theory, an electric field which changes in the course of time with the motion of the electron produces a magnetic field H; the vector product $F \times H$, the Poynting vector, unavoidably leads to an energy loss by radiation which would destroy the atomic structure in a very short time. This contradicts physical facts. London simply assumes that there is an instantaneous field without energy loss by radiation and thus ignores Maxwell's electromagnetic wave theory. Then we know how this field acts as a function of the distance. Since a charge q has a field q/r^2, a dipole, whose moment μ is charge times length, produces a field of μ/r^3, where r is the distance away from the dipole. From (3-3) we find that the potential energy of polarization of another molecule in this instantaneous field is $-(\alpha/2)F^2$. Therefore,

$$E_p = -\frac{\alpha\mu^2}{2r^6} \qquad (3\text{-}7)$$

It may be concluded that there should be a potential energy between the molecules which are attracted to each other, and that this potential energy should decrease with the sixth power of the distance. The forces of attraction, which are the so-called *London forces*, must then be proportional to the seventh power of the reciprocal distance, and exist even if the molecules are symmetrical, i.e., monatomic rare-gas molecules.

Since the original treatment of the wave-mechanical explanation of van der Waals' forces was due to London, the attraction when treated in this way may be termed the *London–van der Waals attraction*. The development for the interaction of two hydrogen atoms over large interatomic distances is as follows.

The attraction between two molecules is due simply to the polarization of each molecule by the other. Consider two linear harmonic oscillators arranged as in Fig. 3-3. The distance R is the equilibrium distance between A and B, and the z axis is chosen parallel to the line through AB. Let (ξ_1, η_1, ζ_1) be the coordinates of electron 1 as measured from positive end A, with r_1 the vector displacement of electron 1 from A; and let (ξ_2, η_2, ζ_2) be the coordinates of electron 2 as measured from positive end B, with r_2 the vector displacement.

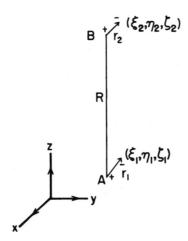

Fig. 3-3. Attraction between two linear harmonic oscillators.

The interaction energy of the system is

$$E_{\text{int}} = e^2 \left(\frac{1}{r_{AB}} + \frac{1}{r_{12}} - \frac{1}{r_{1B}} - \frac{1}{r_{2A}} \right) \tag{3-8}$$

in which the analytical expressions for the distances are

$$r_{AB} = R$$
$$r_{12} = [(\xi_1 - \xi_2)^2 + (\eta_1 - \eta_2)^2 + (\zeta_1 - \zeta_2 - R)^2]^{1/2}$$
$$r_{1B} = [\xi_1^2 + \eta_1^2 + (\zeta_1 - R)^2]^{1/2}$$
$$r_{2A} = [\xi_2^2 + \eta_2^2 + (\zeta_2 + R)^2]^{1/2}$$

We assume that the distance between A and B is very large when compared with the displacement vectors, so that $R \gg \xi_1$, $R \gg \xi_2$, etc. Since

$$(1 + x)^{-1/2} = 1 - \frac{x}{2} + \frac{3}{8} x^2 + \cdots$$

where x is less than 1, we can approximate the distances by expanding in powers of $1/R$ and retaining only the first two powers of the coordinates of the electrons. Thus

$$\frac{1}{r_{AB}} = \frac{1}{R}$$

$$\frac{1}{r_{12}} = \frac{1}{R}\left[1 - \frac{(\xi_1 - \xi_2)^2 + (\eta_1 - \eta_2)^2 - 2(\zeta_1 - \zeta_2)^2 - 2R(\zeta_1 - \zeta_2)}{2R^2}\right]$$

$$\frac{1}{r_{1B}} = \frac{1}{R}\left(1 - \frac{\xi_1^2 + \eta_1^2 - 2\zeta_1^2 - 2R\zeta_1}{2R^2}\right)$$

$$\frac{1}{r_{2A}} = \frac{1}{R}\left(1 - \frac{\xi_2^2 + \eta_2^2 - 2\zeta_2^2 + 2R\zeta_2}{2R^2}\right) \tag{3-9}$$

Stopping the series at terms in $1/R^2$ is equivalent to restricting the forces to dipole interactions. The neglected terms in the expansion that vary like $1/R^4$ and $1/R^6$ correspond to dipole-quadrupole and quadrupole-quadrupole interactions, respectively. After combination of (3-8) and (3-9), we finally get

$$E_{int} = \frac{e^2}{R^3} (\xi_1 \xi_2 + \eta_1 \eta_2 - 2\zeta_1 \zeta_2) \tag{3-10}$$

The quantity E_{int} is the interaction energy of two electric dipoles that corresponds to the instantaneous configuration of the two particles.

Our next step is to calculate the potential energy and the kinetic energy of the two linear harmonic oscillators. If f is the force constant and m the mass of the oscillator, the potential energy due to the oscillators is

$$E_{pot} = \tfrac{1}{2}f(r_1^2 + r_2^2) \tag{3-11}$$

The kinetic energy is

$$E_{kin} = \tfrac{1}{2}m_1\dot{r}_1^2 + \tfrac{1}{2}m_2\dot{r}_2^2 \tag{3-12}$$

in which $\dot{r} = dr/dt$. The total energy of the system is the sum of the kinetic, potential, and interaction energies. After adding these terms, which are (3-10), (3-11), and (3-12), we obtain the result

$$E = \tfrac{1}{2}m_1\dot{r}_1^2 + \tfrac{1}{2}m_2\dot{r}_2^2 + \tfrac{1}{2}f(r_1^2 + r_2^2) + \frac{e^2}{R^3}(\xi_1\xi_2 + \eta_1\eta_2 - 2\zeta_1\zeta_2) \qquad (3\text{-}13)$$

From (3-13) we can see that for large values of R, the last term, which corresponds with the dipole-dipole interaction, is negligible.

Now we want normal coordinates in place of (ξ_1, η_1, ζ_1) and (ξ_2, η_2, ζ_2) so that the energy is separable into terms corresponding with normal modes of vibration. Let

$$\xi_1 = \frac{u_1 + u_2}{2^{1/2}} \qquad \xi_2 = \frac{u_1 - u_2}{2^{1/2}} \qquad \text{etc.}$$

Then

$$\xi_1^2 + \xi_2^2 = u_1^2 + u_2^2 \qquad \xi_1\xi_2 = \frac{u_1^2 - u_2^2}{2}$$

For simplicity, let us take the case of identical harmonic oscillators where $m = m_1 = m_2$. Then the kinetic energy is

$$E_{\text{kin}} = \frac{m}{2}(\dot{u}_1^2 + \dot{v}_1^2 + \dot{w}_1^2 + \dot{u}_2^2 + \dot{v}_2^2 + \dot{w}_2^2)$$

the potential energy is

$$E_{\text{pot}} = \frac{f}{2}(u_1^2 + v_1^2 + w_1^2 + u_2^2 + v_2^2 + w_2^2)$$

and the interaction energy is

$$E_{\text{int}} = \frac{e^2}{2R^3}(u_1^2 + v_1^2 - u_2^2 - v_2^2) - \frac{e^2}{R^3}(w_1^2 - w_2^2)$$

In the new coordinates, the interaction energy as well as the kinetic and potential energies of the two resonators consists of sums of squares only, without any cross terms. Each of the new coordinates is a periodic function involving only one of the resonant frequencies; the system can be represented as six independent vibrators, each with a proper frequency which depends on the strength of the interaction. Lagrange's equations†

---

† Lagrange's equations are discussed in most mechanics texts, e.g., H. Goldstein, *Classical Mechanics*, Addison-Wesley, Reading, Mass., 1950.

are

$$\ddot{u}_1 + \frac{1}{m}\left(f + \frac{e^2}{R^3}\right)u_1 = 0 \qquad \ddot{u}_2 + \frac{1}{m}\left(f - \frac{e^2}{R^3}\right)u_2 = 0$$

$$\ddot{v}_1 + \frac{1}{m}\left(f + \frac{e^2}{R^3}\right)v_1 = 0 \qquad \ddot{v}_2 + \frac{1}{m}\left(f - \frac{e^2}{R^3}\right)v_2 = 0$$

$$\ddot{w}_1 + \frac{1}{m}\left(f - \frac{2e^2}{R^3}\right)w_1 = 0 \qquad \ddot{w}_2 + \frac{1}{m}\left(f + \frac{2e^2}{R^3}\right)w_2 = 0$$

The frequencies are written

$$\omega_1^2 = \begin{cases}\omega_0^2(1+\eta)\\ \omega_0^2(1+\eta)\\ \omega_0^2(1-2\eta)\end{cases} \qquad \omega_2^2 = \begin{cases}\omega_0^2(1-\eta)\\ \omega_0^2(1-\eta)\\ \omega_0^2(1+2\eta)\end{cases}$$

in which $\omega_0^2 = f/m$ and $\eta = e^2/fR^3$. Since η is small compared with unity, we can use the expansions

$$(1 \pm \eta)^{1/2} = 1 \pm \frac{\eta}{2} - \frac{\eta^2}{8} \pm \cdots$$

and get

$$\omega_1 = \begin{cases}\omega_0\left(1+\dfrac{\eta}{2}-\dfrac{\eta^2}{8}\right)\\[2mm] \omega_0\left(1+\dfrac{\eta}{2}-\dfrac{\eta^2}{8}\right)\\[2mm] \omega_0\left(1-\eta-\dfrac{\eta^2}{2}\right)\end{cases} \qquad \omega_2 = \begin{cases}\omega_0\left(1-\dfrac{\eta}{2}-\dfrac{\eta^2}{8}\right)\\[2mm] \omega_0\left(1-\dfrac{\eta}{2}-\dfrac{\eta^2}{8}\right)\\[2mm] \omega_0\left(1+\eta-\dfrac{\eta^2}{2}\right)\end{cases}$$

The complete motion for small oscillations is thus expressed as a super-position of normal modes with different intensities and phase factors.

We shall now introduce the quantum theory and identify the frequencies of the harmonic oscillators with the photon frequencies and the amplitudes of excitation with the number of photons in each frequency. For a one-dimensional harmonic oscillator, we have

$$E_n = (n + \tfrac{1}{2})h\nu_0$$

where $\nu_0 = \omega_0/2\pi$. Hence, for two interacting three-dimensional isotropic harmonic oscillators with vibrational quantum numbers n_1 and n_2, we have

$$E_{n_1 n_2} = \sum_{i=1}^{3} h v_i (n_1 + \tfrac{1}{2}) + \sum_{j=1}^{3} h v_j (n_2 + \tfrac{1}{2})$$

$$= h v_0 (3 - \tfrac{3}{4}\eta^2)(n_1 + \tfrac{1}{2}) + h v_0 (3 - \tfrac{3}{4}\eta^2)(n_2 + \tfrac{1}{2})$$

Suppose $n_1 = n_2 = 0$; then

$$E_{00} = \frac{h v_0}{2} \left(6 - \frac{3}{2}\eta^2 \right) = 3 h v_0 \left(1 - \frac{\eta^2}{4} \right)$$

Now we go back to the case of two identical oscillators. When R is small, the field due to each oscillator acts on the other one. If r is the displacement, then

$$\tfrac{1}{2} f r^2 = \tfrac{1}{2}\alpha F^2$$

Since $\mu = re = \alpha F$, we have $\alpha = e^2/f$. Substituting $\alpha = e^2/f$ in the equation for E_{00}, we obtain

$$E_{00} = 3 h v_0 \left[1 - \left(\frac{\alpha}{2R^3} \right)^2 \right] \tag{3-14}$$

If there is no interaction between the two oscillators, the total energy is given by the term $3 h v_0$, and can be designated E_{00}^*, which is the sum of the six zero-point energies. The quantity E_{00}^* represents the total energy of the system at $T = 0$. Thus (3-14) becomes

$$E_{00} = E_{00}^* - 3 h v_0 \frac{\alpha^2}{4R^6}$$

The coupling energy is $E_{00} - E_{00}^*$:

$$\Delta E = -\tfrac{3}{4} h v_0 \frac{\alpha^2}{R^6} = \frac{-E_{00}^* \alpha^2}{4R^6} \tag{3-15}$$

This shows the energy of interaction between two hydrogen atoms to be inversely proportional to the sixth power of the distance. London identified $h v_0$ with the ionization potential of the atom or molecule.

It may be noted that we can apply these results to the van der Waals model: rigid spheres of radius a with attractive tails where the interaction energy ε is defined by

$$\varepsilon = +\infty \qquad r < 2a$$

$$\varepsilon = -\frac{\Lambda}{r^6} \qquad r > 2a$$

The quantity Λ is a constant and $r \, (\equiv R)$ is the usual separation distance. The second virial coefficient,[†] $B(T)$, is

$$B(T) = \frac{1}{2}\int_0^\infty (1 - e^{-\varepsilon/kT})4\pi r^2 \, dr$$

$$= 4 \cdot \frac{4}{3}\pi a^3 + 2\pi \int_{2a}^\infty (1 - e^{\Lambda/r^6 kT})r^2 \, dr$$

Suppose $\Lambda/r^6 kT \ll 1$; then $\exp(\Lambda/r^6 kT) \simeq 1 + (\Lambda/r^6 kT)$ and

$$B(T) = 4 \cdot \frac{4}{3}\pi a^3 - 2\pi \int_{2a}^\infty \left(\frac{\Lambda}{kTr^4}\right) dr$$

$$= 4 \cdot \frac{4}{3}\pi a^3 - \frac{\pi\Lambda}{12kTa^3}$$

$$= 4 \cdot \frac{4}{3}\pi a^3 - \frac{\pi}{16kT}hv_0\alpha^2 \frac{1}{a^3}$$

3-5. ZERO-POINT ENERGY

The consideration of an instantaneous field leads to the conclusion that molecular forces are connected with the motions of charges in the interior of a molecule. It should be emphasized that interaction between molecules will occur only if there is an electric field, and movements of the electrons which produce the electric field cannot be "frozen" in, even at absolute zero. Thus there exists a zero-point energy even at $T = 0$. Another conclusion to be drawn from this explanation of van der Waals' attraction is that the molecular interaction energy should depend upon temperature. The interacting systems would have a series of energy levels, each with its own electric field, whereas the population of such levels would change with temperature. For instance, at absolute zero, the electrons are all in the lowest energy level, and only zero-point energy exists in a resonator. But the energy increases with temperature, and so at higher temperatures there is a different electric field which changes the forces of attraction between

† According to the Leiden school, the virial equation

$$\frac{PV}{NkT} = 1 + \frac{B(T)}{V} + \frac{C(T)}{V^2} + \cdots$$

is expressed in terms of a series expansion involving powers of the reciprocal of the volume multiplied by coefficients which are functions of temperature. $B(T)$, $C(T)$, ... are the second, third, ... virial coefficients. If the gas is ideal, $PV/NkT = 1$.

the resonators (or molecules). No experiments on the temperature dependence of the molecular forces of attraction have yet been performed.

Let us now reminisce about the historical developments which led to the idea of zero-point energy, even though they are no longer important to the understanding of molecular forces.

A. Stefan-Boltzmann Law (1879)

First of all there was the equation of Stefan and Boltzmann for black-body radiation. A *black body* is one that absorbs all radiation and has an absorption coefficient of unity. A practical way of making a black body is to use a cavity with a small hole in it; when radiation gets into the hole, it has difficulty getting out. Thus a cavity with a small hole would absorb all radiation. In investigating the light (or energy) which comes out of the hole in the cavity at different temperatures, Stefan concluded from certain measurements of Tyndall that the total intensity (or energy flux) from a surface varies with the fourth power of the absolute temperature; i.e.,

$$E(\text{flux}) = \sigma T^4 \tag{3-16}$$

in which $E(\text{flux})$ is the total energy radiated per unit area per unit time and T is the temperature of the radiator in absolute units. Equation (3-16) was subsequently derived theoretically for black-body radiation by Boltzmann (2) and is known as the Stefan-Boltzmann law. It is an expression for the total energy flux emerging from an opening in a furnace (black body).

B. Radiation Laws of Planck, Rayleigh-Jeans, and Wien

How is the energy which comes from a hot body distributed over the frequencies?

In our present discussion we are going to consider electromagnetic vibrations of harmonic oscillators. A vacuous cavity can contain only electric and magnetic energies, analogous to the kinetic and potential energies of harmonic oscillators. The boundary condition which applies when the waves reflect back and forth between the walls of a cubical cavity requires that waves have modes at the surfaces of the cavity. For a system of electromagnetic vibrations with wavelength λ, velocity of propagation c, and frequency $v\,(= c/\lambda)$, the number of modes of proper vibrations per unit volume with frequencies in the range v to $v + dv$ is

$$dn_l = \frac{4\pi v^2 \, dv}{c^3}$$

However, this dn_l refers to the longitudinal vibrations. Radiation in a cavity does not consist of longitudinal vibrations but of two mutually perpendicular transverse vibrations in a plane at right angles to the direction of wave propagation. Hence the number of modes of proper vibrations per cubic centimeter (or the number of oscillators of frequency v per cubic centimeter) is

$$dn = 2 \cdot \frac{4\pi v^2 \, dv}{c^3} = \frac{8\pi v^2 \, dv}{c^3}$$

Following the principle of equipartition of energy, Rayleigh (*3*) and Jeans (*4*) took the mean energy per vibration $\bar{\varepsilon}$ to be kT with $\frac{1}{2}kT$ for the electric term and $\frac{1}{2}kT$ for the magnetic term. Thus the total energy density of radiation in the frequency range of v to $v + dv$ is

$$u(v, T) = \frac{8\pi v^2 kT}{c^3} dv \tag{3-17}$$

in which T is the temperature of the cavity wall. However, (3-17) must fail, since it requires the total energy per cubic centimeter to be infinitely large:

$$u(T) = \int_0^\infty \frac{8\pi kT}{c^3} v^2 \, dv = \infty! \tag{3-18}$$

Accordingly, the specific heat of a vacuous cavity, which is $[\partial u(T)/\partial T]_V$, would also be infinite. This implies that it should be impossible to raise the temperature of a vacuous cavity. Since the divergence of the integral [Eq. (3-18)] is caused by vibrations of high frequencies (large v), this was sometimes referred to as the "violet catastrophy." The radiation formula (3-17) holds only for the red end of the spectrum.

The violet catastrophy was ultimately resolved by Planck (*5*), who assumed that an oscillator can take up energy only discontinuously, in multiples of a unit quantum ε_0. We shall sketch Planck's derivation as follows. Let N_0 be the number of oscillators of the lowest energy, and N be the total number of oscillators, possessing different amounts of energy, $0, \varepsilon_0, 2\varepsilon_0, 3\varepsilon_0, \ldots$, etc. Then according to the Maxwell-Boltzmann distribution law,

$$N = N_0 \sum_{n=0}^{\infty} e^{-n\varepsilon_0/kT}$$

Planck further assumed that each unit quantum which the oscillator can emit or absorb is proportional to its frequency v; in other words,

$$\varepsilon_0 = hv$$

where h is a universal constant. Thus the total energy of the oscillators E is

$$E = N_0 \sum_{n=0}^{\infty} n\varepsilon_0 e^{-n\varepsilon_0/kT} = N_0 \sum_{n=0}^{\infty} nh\nu e^{-nh\nu/kT}$$

The average energy of each oscillator (in excess of the zero-point energy) is then

$$\bar{\varepsilon} = \frac{E}{N} = \frac{h\nu \sum_{n=0}^{\infty} ne^{-n(h\nu/kT)}}{\sum_{n=0}^{\infty} e^{-n(h\nu/kT)}} = \frac{h\nu}{e^{h\nu/kT} - 1}$$

Thus Planck's radiation formula states that the total energy density of radiation in the frequency range of ν to $\nu + d\nu$ is

$$u(\nu, T) = \frac{8\pi\nu^2}{c^3} \frac{h\nu}{e^{h\nu/kT} - 1} d\nu \qquad (3-19)$$

If $h\nu/kT$ is small (red region),

$$u(\nu, T)d\nu = \frac{8\pi h\nu^3}{c^3} \frac{d\nu}{1 + (h\nu/kT) + \cdots - 1} = \frac{8\pi\nu^2}{c^3} kT\, d\nu \qquad (3-20a)$$

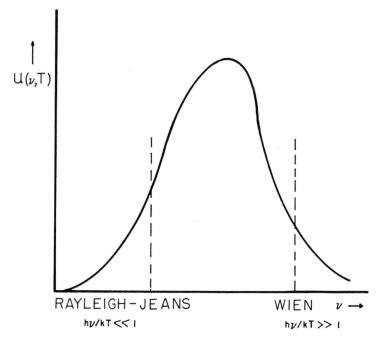

RAYLEIGH–JEANS   WIEN $\nu \longrightarrow$

$h\nu/kT \ll 1$ $h\nu/kT \gg 1$

Fig. 3-4. Planck's radiation law.

which is the radiation law of Rayleigh-Jeans. If hv/kT is large,

$$u(v, T)dv = \frac{8\pi hv^3}{c^3} e^{-hv/kT} dv \tag{3-20b}$$

Equation (3-20b) is Wien's law (6), which holds for the violet part of the radiation spectrum (Fig. 3-4).

From Planck's radiation formula, the total energy density for all frequencies is obtained as

$$u(T) = \int_0^\infty \frac{8\pi hv^3}{c^3} \frac{dv}{e^{hv/kT} - 1} = \int_0^\infty \frac{8\pi k^4 T^4}{c^3 h^3} \frac{x^3 \, dx}{e^x - 1}$$

where $x = hv/kT$. With the integral $\int_0^\infty x^3 \, dx/(e^x - 1)$ evaluated,†

$$u(T) = \frac{8\pi^5 k^4 T^4}{15 c^3 h^3} = aT^4$$

with

$$a = \frac{8\pi^5 k^4}{15 c^3 h^3} = 7.64 \times 10^{-15} \text{ erg cm}^{-3} \text{ deg}^{-4}$$

The energy flux E passing through an opening of 1 cm² in the wall of an oven is‡

$$E(\text{flux}) = \frac{c}{4} u$$

---

† Evaluation of the integral $\int_0^\infty x^3 \, dx/(e^x - 1)$ is as follows:

$$\frac{1}{e^x - 1} = e^{-x} + e^{-2x} + e^{-3x} + \cdots$$

$$\int_0^\infty \frac{x^3 \, dx}{e^x - 1} = \int_0^\infty x^3(e^{-x} + e^{-2x} + e^{-3x} + \cdots) \, dx$$

$$\int_0^\infty x^3 e^{-nx} \, dx = \frac{6}{n^4}$$

and

$$\sum_{n=1}^\infty \frac{1}{n^4} = 1 + \frac{1}{2^4} + \frac{1}{3^4} + \cdots = \frac{\pi^4}{90}$$

So, we obtain $\int_0^\infty x^3 \, dx/(e^x - 1) = \pi^4/15$.

‡ Energy transfer by radiation is discussed in J. O. Hirschfelder, R. B. Bird, and C. F. Curtiss, *Molecular Theory of Gases and Liquids*, Wiley, New York, 1954, pp. 720–727.

in which u is the energy density of radiation. Thus

$$E(\text{flux}) = \frac{2\pi^5 k^4 T^4}{15c^2 h^3} = \sigma T^4$$

This shows that the σ in the Stefan-Boltzmann law is equal to $2\pi^5 k^4 / 15c^2 h^3$.

In Planck's derivation, there is an obvious weakness in the argument because he denies the validity of the principle of equipartition, yet assumes the validity of the electrodynamical equations. Both could be deduced from the fundamental dynamical equations of classical mechanics. Planck is saying that a resonator which obeys laws of classical mechanics can pick up energy only in quanta. This means that energy is divisible as far as we want, but, on the other hand, it exists only in multiples of a unit quantum ε_0 which is equal to hv.

C. Planck's Formula and Zero-Point Energy

Planck also introduced a zero-point energy, $hv/2$, without theoretical justification. We can see how he derived this quantity by considering the old formula for the average energy of an oscillator, $\bar{\varepsilon} = hv/(e^{hv/kT} - 1)$. We may write

$$\frac{hv}{e^{hv/kT} - 1} = kT\frac{x}{e^x - 1} \simeq kT \tag{3-21}$$

in which $x = hv/kT$. At high temperatures, when $hv/kT \ll 1$, we may also write

$$\frac{hv}{e^{hv/kT} - 1} \simeq kT\frac{1}{1 + (x/2)} = kT(1 - \tfrac{1}{2}x)$$

$$= kT\left(1 - \frac{1}{2}\frac{hv}{kT}\right) = kT - \frac{hv}{2} \tag{3-22}$$

Equation (3-22) tells us that at high temperatures the average energy of the oscillator $\bar{\varepsilon}$ is $kT - (hv/2)$ instead of the equipartition energy kT, which tells us that there is no interaction when $T = 0$. But we know that at high temperatures the principle of equipartition of energy holds. In order to have kT at high temperatures, $\bar{\varepsilon}$ must have the following form:

$$\bar{\varepsilon} = \frac{hv}{2} + \frac{hv}{e^{hv/kT} - 1} \tag{3-23}$$

Equation (3-23) tells us that $\bar{\varepsilon} = kT$ when $hv/kT \ll 1$; and $\bar{\varepsilon} = hv/2$ when $T = 0$, as shown in Fig. 3-5. The quantity $hv/2$ is the zero-point energy; it

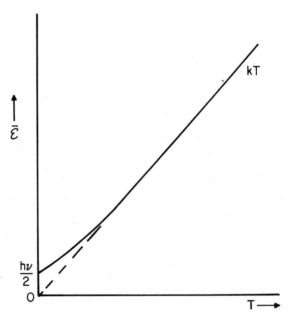

Fig. 3-5. Planck's radiation law and zero-point energy.

is responsible for molecular interactions between resonators and is actually the interior energy of a resonator. In addition, if there is a zero-point energy, atoms in a solid should also have an indefiniteness of position, even at absolute zero temperature. The average amplitude of the motion of atoms in a crystal lattice can be determined by measuring the scattered intensities of X rays at different temperatures. Bragg has concluded from such measurements that an indefiniteness of position does exist even at absolute zero. In other words, atoms are like vibrators and do not stand still at absolute zero.

Now we should be convinced that there is a zero-point energy.

REFERENCES

1. P. Debye, *Physik. Z.*, **21**, 178 (1920).
2. L. Boltzmann, *Ann. Physik Chem.*, **22**, 31, 291, 616 (1884).
3. Lord J. W. S. Rayleigh, *Phil. Mag.*, **49**, 539 (1900); through J. R. Partington, *An Advanced Treatise on Physical Chemistry*, Vol. I, Longmans, Green, London, 1949, p. 484.
4. J. H. Jeans, *Phil. Mag.*, **10**, 91 (1905).
5. M. Planck, *Ann. Physik Chem.*, **4**, 553 (1901).
6. W. Wien, *Ann. Physik Chem.*, **58**, 662 (1896).

CHAPTER

MOLECULAR INTERACTION AND COLLOID CHEMISTRY

4-1. INTRODUCTION

In 1932 Kallman and Willstatter (*1*) remarked that the attractive inter-action between colloidal particles could probably be the integrated van der Waals attraction of their constituent atoms or molecules. In the next 10 to 15 years this idea was applied to colloidal solutions; a book of Verwey and Overbeek (*2*) gives an excellent survey on the theory of the stability of lyophobic colloids.

In 1936 and 1937 de Boer (*3*) and Hamaker (*4*) calculated the interaction between spherical particles, assuming that the interaction between atoms obeys London's theory. A total interaction energy was obtained by per-forming a double summation over all the atoms contained in both spheres. To discuss the stability of lyophobic colloids, the van der Waals interaction energy obtained in this way has to be combined with the electrical inter-action energy due to the presence of electrolyte in the liquid surrounding the colloidal particles. We shall first consider the van der Waals interaction and base our calculations on the assumption that the van der Waals forces between big assemblies of particles can be obtained by just adding up the interactions between single particles. Such calculations are not quite right, but will serve to illustrate the use of van der Waals' forces in explaining colloid stability. Then we shall utilize our results in Chapter 2 and proceed to compute the electrostatic repulsion for particles in an electrolyte solution. The stability conditions for colloids can be derived from the nature of the total potential-energy curve, which is a sum of molecular attraction and electrostatic repulsion.

4-2. APPLICATION OF THE LONDON–VAN DER WAALS ATTRACTION TO COLLOIDAL PARTICLES

In our application of London–van der Waals' forces to colloids, we shall consider the energy of interaction between particles which have well-defined geometric shapes and uniform densities, so that integration over the volumes of both particles may readily be performed.

According to London's theory, electrically neutral and symmetrical atoms (or molecules) have instantaneous dipoles which induce dipoles in neighboring atoms (or molecules) and vice versa. The resulting attractive force, from the reciprocal action between the induced and the inducing dipoles, is proportional to $1/r^7$, in which r is the separation distance between two atoms (or molecules). The energy of interaction between two atoms (or molecules) due to London's forces is

$$\varepsilon = -\frac{\Lambda}{r^6}$$

where Λ is a coupling constant dependent on the properties of the atoms (or molecules). Thus the energy of interaction between two particles, each containing n atoms per cubic centimeter, is

$$W_A = -\int_{V_1} d\tau_1 \int_{V_2} d\tau_2 \frac{n^2 \Lambda}{r^6} \tag{4-1}$$

where r is the distance between $d\tau_1$ and $d\tau_2$; $d\tau_1$, $d\tau_2$, V_1, and V_2 denote volume elements and total volumes of particles 1 and 2, respectively. It appears rather difficult to express the constant Λ completely in terms of physical constants of the atoms, but rough approximate equations have been proposed. One of them is the London–van der Waals constant:

$$\Lambda = \tfrac{3}{4}h\nu_0\alpha^2$$

in which $h\nu_0$ is the ionization energy of the atom and α is the polarizability.

A. Attraction between Two Spherical Particles

Suppose we have a point P at a distance $OP = d$ from the center of a sphere O of radius a_1 (see Fig. 4-1). The surface ABC, S_{ABC}, cut out from a sphere of radius r around P by the sphere around O is

$$S_{ABC} = 2\pi \int_0^{\theta_0} r^2 \sin \theta \, d\theta$$

where θ_0 has the relation $a_1^2 = d^2 + r^2 - 2rd \cos \theta_0$. Thus

$$S_{ABC} = \frac{\pi r}{d} [a_1^2 - (d - r)^2]$$

and since $d\tau_1 = S_{ABC} \, dr$, the potential energy of interaction of an atom at P due to a spherical particle with its center at O is

$$E_P = -\int_{d-a_1}^{d+a_1} \frac{\Lambda n\pi}{r^6} \frac{r}{d} [a_1^2 - (d - r)^2] \, dr$$

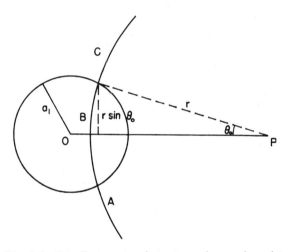

Fig. 4-1. Coordinate system between a sphere and a point.

Then, according to (4-1), the total energy of interaction between two spheres with their centers a distance R apart is

$$W_A = \int_{R-a_2}^{R+a_2} E_P n\pi \frac{d}{R} [a_2^2 - (R - d)^2] \, dd$$

Carrying out the integrations, we get

$$W_A = -\frac{n^2\pi^2\Lambda}{R}\int_{R-a_2}^{R+a_2}[a_2^2-(R-d)^2]\left[\int_{d-a_1}^{d+a_1}\frac{a_1^2-(d-r)^2}{r^5}\,dr\right]dd$$

$$= -\frac{n^2\pi^2\Lambda}{R}\int_{R-a_2}^{R+a_2}[a_2^2-(R-d)^2]\frac{1}{12}\left[\frac{2a_1}{(d+a_1)^3}+\frac{2a_1}{(d-a_1)^3}\right.$$

$$\left.+\frac{1}{(d+a_1)^2}-\frac{1}{(d-a_1)^2}\right]dd$$

$$= -\frac{n^2\pi^2\Lambda}{6}\left[\frac{2a_1a_2}{R^2-(a_1+a_2)^2}+\frac{2a_1a_2}{R^2-(a_1-a_2)^2}+\ln\frac{R^2-(a_1+a_2)^2}{R^2-(a_1-a_2)^2}\right]$$

$$(4\text{-}2)$$

When two spheres have equal size, $a_1 = a_2 = a$. Equation (4-2) reduces to

$$W_A = -\frac{A}{6}\left[\frac{2a^2}{R^2-4a^2}+\frac{2a^2}{R^2}+\ln\left(1-\frac{4a^2}{R^2}\right)\right]$$

with $A = n^2\pi^2\Lambda$. We are interested in this interaction energy especially when the distance between the two spheres is either very small or very large. When $R \simeq 2a$,

$$W_A \simeq -\frac{A}{12}\frac{a}{S}\qquad(4\text{-}3)$$

where $S(= R - 2a$, as shown in Fig. 4-2) represents the shortest distance between the surfaces of the two particles. The potential energy increases as one over the distance between the surfaces, and becomes infinite at the point where the particles touch. Figure 4-3 shows an approximation of the behavior of W_A as a function of distance S for $R \simeq 2a$. When $R \gg 2a$,

$$W_A \simeq -\frac{16A}{9}\frac{a^6}{S^6}\qquad(4\text{-}4)$$

B. Attraction between a Flat Surface and a Spherical Particle

We now introduce the quantities $x = S/2a$ and $y = a_2/a_1$. When $y = \infty$, we have the case of a sphere and an infinite mass bounded by a flat surface (Fig. 4-4). The interaction energy is

$$W_A\,(y = \infty) = -\frac{A}{12}\left(\frac{1}{x}+\frac{1}{1+x}+2\ln\frac{x}{1+x}\right)\qquad(4\text{-}5)$$

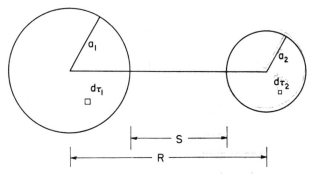

Fig. 4-2. Coordinate system between two spheres.

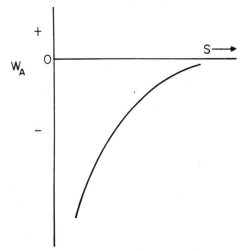

Fig. 4-3. An approximation of the behavior of the attractive energy of interaction W_A, between two macroscopic spheres as a function of separation distance S for very small S (schematic).

When $x \ll 1$, we then have, with $a \equiv a_1$,

$$W_A (y = \infty) \simeq -\frac{A\,a}{6\,S} \tag{4-6}$$

From (4-6) and (4-3) it may be noted that $W_A (y = \infty) = 2W_A (y = 1)$ for small S.

The expressions for force, $-\partial W_A/\partial S$, are: when $y = 1$, and $R \simeq 2a$, $F_A (y = 1) \simeq -(A/12)(a/S^2)$; and when $y = \infty$, and $x \ll 1$, $F_A (y = \infty) \simeq -(A/6)(a/S^2)$. Thus a enters explicitly in the formulas.

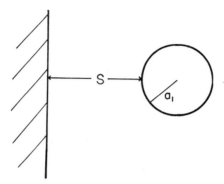

Fig. 4-4. Coordinate system between a sphere and a flat surface.

Theoretically, (4-6) relates only to an infinite mass bounded by a flat surface. In practice, we may use (4-6) for interactions between a plate of finite thickness and a sphere of radius a, as shown in Fig. 4-5. The energy of interaction is $W_A(x_1) - W_A(x_2)$, where $x_1 = d_1/2a$ and $x_2 = d_2/2a$; d_1 and d_2 are the shortest distances between the surface of the sphere and the front and back surfaces of the flat plate, respectively. If the sphere is close to the flat plate, then $x_2 \gg x_1$ and $W_A(x_2) \ll W_A(x_1)$. If the sphere is further away, $W_A(x_1) - W_A(x_2)$ becomes small. Thus the energy will be determined mainly by the size of the smaller of the two particles.

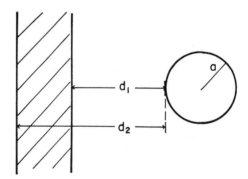

Fig. 4-5. Coordinate system between a sphere and a plate of finite thickness.

C. Attraction between Two Flat Plates

Other calculations, such as for attractions between plates and between a single atom (or molecule) and a flat surface (*3, 5*) have been performed.

For a single atom (or molecule) at a distance d from a flat surface, the attractive force is

$$F_A = -\iiint \frac{6\Lambda n}{r^7} \cos\phi \, d\tau$$

$$= -12\pi n\Lambda \int_0^{\pi/2} \sin\phi \cos\phi \, d\phi \int_{d/\cos\phi}^{\infty} \frac{r^2 \, dr}{r^7}$$

$$= -\frac{3\pi n\Lambda}{d^4} \int_0^{\pi/2} \sin\phi \cos^5\phi \, d\phi$$

If we let $x = \cos\phi$,

$$F_A = -\frac{3\pi n\Lambda}{d^4} \int_1^0 (-x^5) \, dx = -\frac{n\pi\Lambda}{2d^4}$$

Accordingly,

$$E_P = -\frac{n\pi\Lambda}{6} \frac{1}{d^3}$$

The energy of interaction per square centimeter between two flat surfaces at a distance d apart is

$$W_A = -\int_d^{\infty} \frac{n\pi\Lambda}{6} \frac{1}{r^3} n \, dr = -\frac{A}{12\pi} \frac{1}{d^2}$$

Thus the force per square centimeter is

$$F = -\frac{A}{6\pi} \frac{1}{d^3}$$

By inserting practical values for the fundamental quantities $h\nu_0$, α, and n, we find that the force per square centimeter of plate surface F should be somewhere between $F = -0.02/d_\mu^3$ and $-0.4/d_\mu^3$ dynes/cm², in which the distance d_μ is measured in microns.

4-3. ATTRACTIONS PROPORTIONAL TO $1/r^q$ (4)

Suppose the interaction energy between two atoms is $-\Lambda/r^q$. The interaction energy of volume elements $d\tau_1$ and $d\tau_2$, one in each of two particles, at a distance r apart, is

$$dW_A = -\frac{\Lambda n^2 \, d\tau_1 \, d\tau_2}{r^q}$$

where n is the number of atoms per cubic centimeter. If we now increase all geometric dimensions by a factor c, the contribution by the corresponding volume elements $d\tau_1'$ and $d\tau_2'$ in the new configuration will be

$$dW_A' = -\frac{\Lambda n^2 \, d\tau_1' \, d\tau_2'}{(r')^q} = -\frac{\Lambda n^2 c^3 \, d\tau_1 c^3 \, d\tau_2}{c^q r^q} = \frac{dW_A}{c^{q-6}}$$

Since each elementary part of the energy has changed in the ratio $1/c^{q-6}$, the same proportional change will hold for the total energy. Therefore, if we change the size of the particles by the factor c and put them c times as far apart, the energy of interaction changes as $1/c^{q-6}$; this energy remains constant when $q = 6$, decreases when q is greater than 6, and increases when q is less than 6.

We may note from the above consideration that the force of gravity, which is negligibly small when acting between atoms or colloidal particles, predominates in celestial mechanics.

4-4. ELECTRICAL REPULSION BETWEEN PARTICLES IN ELECTROLYTE SOLUTIONS

A. Repulsion between Two Flat Plates

For particles in an electrolyte solution, there may also exist a repulsion due to the formation of a "double layer" of ions, in addition to molecular attractions. A double layer of ions on a surface comes from an unequal distribution of positive and negative ions. The force due to the interaction of double layers may be derived in several ways (6–8).

Consider two infinitely large parallel plates immersed in an electrolyte solution as shown in Fig. 4-6. At equilibrium the force on the space charge $\rho\nabla\phi$, and the gradient of the hydrostatic pressure ∇P balance each other. In addition, with two infinitely large parallel plates, the hydrostatic pressure P, the charge density ρ, and the electrostatic potential ϕ are functions of x only. Thus

$$-\frac{dP}{dx} = \rho\frac{d\phi}{dx} \tag{4-7}$$

From Poisson's equation, we know that

$$\rho = -\frac{d^2\phi}{dx^2}\frac{\epsilon}{4\pi}$$

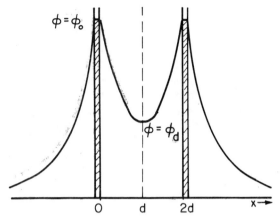

$\phi = \phi_0$

$\phi = \phi_d$

O   d   2d   x⟶

Fig. 4-6. Schematic representation of the electric potential ϕ between two infinitely large parallel plates at a distance $2d$ apart.

in which ϵ is the dielectric constant of the medium. Then

$$\frac{dP}{dx} = \frac{\epsilon}{4\pi}\frac{d\phi}{dx}\frac{d^2\phi}{dx^2} = \frac{\epsilon}{8\pi}\frac{d}{dx}\left[\left(\frac{d\phi}{dx}\right)^2\right]$$

or

$$P = \frac{\epsilon}{8\pi}\left(\frac{d\phi}{dx}\right)^2 + \text{constant} \qquad (4\text{-}8)$$

Equation (4-8) tells us that the difference between the hydrostatic pressure and Maxwell's stresses is a constant everywhere. The boundary conditions require that $\phi = \phi_d$ and $d\phi/dx = 0$ midway between the two plates where $x = d$. We shall define P_d as the hydrostatic pressure at $x = d$. The force acting on 1 cm² of the phase boundary of *one* plate due to the double-layer interaction must be $p = P_d - P_\infty$, in which P_∞ is the hydrostatic pressure for $x = \infty$. This pressure difference is the force which tends to drive the plates apart. With (4-7) and (2-5) we have

$$p = \int_{P_\infty}^{P_d} dp$$

$$= -\int_0^{\phi_d} \rho \, d\phi$$

$$= -\int_0^{\phi_d} - 2n^0 e\left(\sinh\frac{e\phi}{kT}\right) d\phi$$

$$= 2n^0 kT\left(\cosh\frac{e\phi_d}{kT} - 1\right) \qquad (4\text{-}9)$$

in which n^0 is the number of positive (or negative) ions per cubic centimeter far from the central ion and e the elementary charge. Equation (4-9) is applicable to the case of uni-univalent electrolytes and is based on a double-layer theory, where the ions in solution are in equilibrium due to "osmotic" and electrostatic forces. It may be noted that this expression for the force acting between two plates due to the interaction of the double layers has no explicit terms for the separation distance and the electrostatic surface potential ϕ_0 (see Fig. 4-6), but depends only on ϕ_d, the electrostatic potential midway between the plates. Since $p = -\partial W/\partial x$, the repulsive potential between two infinitely large parallel plates is

$$W_E \text{ (parallel plates)} = -2 \int_\infty^d p \, dx \qquad (4\text{-}10)$$

W_E corresponds to the work necessary to bring two plates which are infinitely apart to a separation distance of $2d$. In the case of small interaction, ϕ_d will be small, so that $e\phi_d/kT < 1$, and

$$\cosh \frac{e\phi_d}{kT} \simeq 1 + \frac{1}{2!}\left(\frac{e\phi_d}{kT}\right)^2 + \frac{1}{4!}\left(\frac{e\phi_d}{kT}\right)^4 + \cdots \dagger$$

Equation (4-9) can be reduced from $p = 2n^0kT[\cosh(e\phi_d/kT) - 1]$ to

$$p \simeq 2n^0kT\left[\left(\frac{e\phi_d}{kT}\right)^2\frac{1}{2!} + \cdots\right] = n^0kT\left(\frac{e\phi_d}{kT}\right)^2 \qquad (4\text{-}11)$$

To get W_E (parallel plates) we have to know the relation between ϕ_d and d. From (2-1) and (2-5) we have the fundamental differential equation for a flat double layer:

$$\frac{d^2y}{d\xi^2} = \sinh y \qquad (4\text{-}12)$$

in which $y = e\phi/kT$, $\xi = \kappa x$, and $\kappa^2 = 8\pi n^0 e^2/\epsilon kT$. Remembering that $\sinh y = \frac{1}{2}(e^y - e^{-y})$, we find

$$\frac{d}{d\xi}\left(\frac{dy}{d\xi}\right)^2 = (e^y - e^{-y})\frac{dy}{d\xi}$$

Thus

$$\left(\frac{dy}{d\xi}\right)^2 = e^y + e^{-y} + C$$

$$\dagger \cosh u = \frac{e^u + e^{-u}}{2} = \frac{1}{2}\left(1 + u + \frac{u^2}{2!} + \cdots + 1 - u + \frac{u^2}{2!} - \frac{u^3}{3!} + \cdots\right)$$

$$= 1 + \frac{u^2}{2!} + \frac{u^4}{4!} + \cdots$$

In the central plane, $y = u = e\phi_d/kT$, $dy/d\xi = 0$, for $x = d$. We then have

$$C = -2 \cosh u$$

and

$$\frac{dy}{d\xi} = -(2 \cosh y - 2 \cosh u)^{1/2} \qquad (4\text{-}13)$$

We take the minus sign before the square root because $dy/d\xi$ is negative for positive y. Equation (4-13) is integrated a second time between the limits $x = 0$ and $x = d$:

$$\int_z^u \frac{dy}{(2 \cosh y - 2 \cosh u)^{1/2}} = -\int_0^{\kappa d} d\xi = -\kappa d \qquad (4\text{-}14)$$

in which $z = e\phi_0/kT$ for $x = 0$. This integral (4-14) leads to an elliptic integral of the first kind and can be solved numerically. However, if the interaction is small, we may approximate ϕ_d as the sum of two unperturbed double layers.

For a flat double layer, the boundary conditions are $y_1 = 0$ and $dy_1/d\xi = 0$ for $\xi = \infty$. The subscript 1 denotes one flat double layer. Thus $C_1 = -2$, and

$$\frac{dy_1}{d\xi} = -(e^{y_1} + e^{-y_1} - 2)^{1/2} = -2 \sinh \frac{y_1}{2} \qquad (4\text{-}15)$$

Let $\alpha = e^{y_1/2}$. Then

$$-d\xi = d \ln(\alpha - 1) - d \ln(\alpha + 1)$$

On integration between the limits $x = 0$ and $x = x$, we obtain

$$-\xi = \ln \frac{e^{y_1/2} - 1}{e^{y_1/2} + 1} - \ln \frac{e^{z/2} - 1}{e^{z/2} + 1} \qquad (4\text{-}16a)$$

or

$$y_1 = 2 \ln \frac{1 + \gamma e^{-\xi}}{1 - \gamma e^{-\xi}} \qquad (4\text{-}16b)$$

where $\gamma = (e^{z/2} - 1)/(e^{z/2} + 1)$. For arbitrary values of z and large plate-separation distance $(2d)$, $\xi \gg 1$, we then have

$$y_1 \simeq 2 \ln(1 + 2\gamma e^{-\xi})$$

If $\xi \gg 1$, we may assume $|2\gamma e^{-\xi}| < 1$, so that

$$y_1 \simeq 4\gamma e^{-\xi} \qquad (4\text{-}17)$$

for a single flat double layer. According to (4-17) we get

$$y_1 = ze^{-\zeta} \quad \text{or} \quad \phi_1 = \phi_0 e^{-\kappa x}$$

when $z \ll 1$, and

$$y_1 = 4e^{-\zeta} \quad \text{or} \quad \phi_1 = \frac{4kT}{e} e^{-\kappa x}$$

when $z \gg 1$. Now we may approximate the potential for the case of two flat double layers in interaction as the sum of two unperturbed double layers,

$$u = 2y_{1d} \qquad \text{(small interaction)} \tag{4-18}$$

where $y_{1d} = e\phi_{1d}/kT$, and ϕ_{1d} is the electrostatic potential for a single flat double layer at a distance d from the surface. Substituting (4-17) and (4-18) in (4-11), we find for the repulsive force acting on 1 cm^2 of the phase boundary of one plate due to the double-layer interaction,

$$P = 64n^0 kT\gamma^2 e^{-2\kappa d}$$

and thus, for the repulsive potential from (4-10),

$$W_E \text{ (parallel plates)} = 64n^0 kT\gamma^2 2 \int_d^\infty e^{-2\kappa d} \, dd$$

$$= \frac{64n^0 kT}{\kappa} \gamma^2 e^{-2\kappa d} \qquad \text{(small interaction)} \tag{4-19}$$

B. Repulsion between Two Spherical Particles

The calculation of the electric repulsion between spherical particles in an electrolyte solution is very long. We shall first give a qualitative picture.

It is too naïve to assume that the charged particles in a medium containing electrolytes really act on each other as simple charged bodies, because the charge is actually shielded by an ionic atmosphere. This atmosphere comes from the electrolyte, which distributes in such a way that there is a concentration of oppositely charged ions around a charged surface. The ionic atmosphere is characterized by the constant κ, defined as

$$\kappa^2 = \frac{1}{\lambda^2} = \frac{4\pi}{\epsilon kT} \sum n_i e_i^2$$

where λ is the thickness of the ionic atmosphere, n_i the number of ions per cubic centimeter of kind i, e the charge of each ion of kind i, and ϵ the dielectric constant of the medium. For example, $\lambda \simeq 100$ A in a millimolar aqueous solution of a uni-univalent electrolyte. Suppose we have particles with a diameter of about 1μ (10^4 A). The charged particles in a medium containing electrolytes do not interact until they come in the neighborhood of each other, in this case to a distance of about 100 A apart, because at greater distances the charges are counteracted by the ionic atmosphere. So we come to the conclusion that the repulsive electrostatic interaction of such particles exists only at very small distances. If we could actually look at particles which are stabilized by electrical charges, e.g., ions in electrolyte solutions, we would see that the colloidal particles do not really hit each other. They approach each other to a distance of perhaps 50 or 20 A and then they go apart. They never touch except on rare occasions.

Consider two spheres of radius a. If S is the shortest distance between surfaces, then the distance between centers is R, which is equal to $2a + S$. The expression for repulsive electrostatic potential may be obtained by essentially the same method we used for the case of two flat plates. The final result for spherical particles with small κa is

$$W_E = \frac{\epsilon a^2}{R} \, \phi_0^2 e^{-\kappa S} \tag{4-20}$$

in which ϕ_0 is usually designated as the zeta potential (ζ). The magnitude of the intercept on W_E in a plot of W_E versus S depends on ϕ_0.

4-5. STABILITY CONDITIONS FOR COLLOIDS

A. Stability

The stability conditions for colloids can be derived from considerations of the total potential-energy curve as a function of the distance S. The total potential energy is a superposition of two separate potential energies due to (a) van der Waal's (attractive) forces and (b) the electrostatic (repulsive) forces. For $R \simeq 2a$,

$$W = W_A + W_E = -\frac{A}{12}\frac{a}{S} + \frac{\epsilon a^2}{R} \zeta^2 e^{-\kappa S} \tag{4-21}$$

Figure 4-7 is a plot of W versus S. The shape of the total potential-energy curve depends on the zeta potential of the particle. If ζ gets bigger, then W_E, which is proportional to ζ^2, gets bigger. Also, because the total interaction energy is the sum of W_E and W_A, we can make ζ so big that a maximum appears in the W versus S plot. At large distances W is attractive, because W_A is proportional to $1/S^6$, (4-4), whereas W_E decreases exponentially, (4-20). On the other hand, the exponential behavior of W_E overshadows W_A when S gets sufficiently small, and W becomes repulsive. However, W_A eventually wins over, because W_E is finite at $S = 0$. The

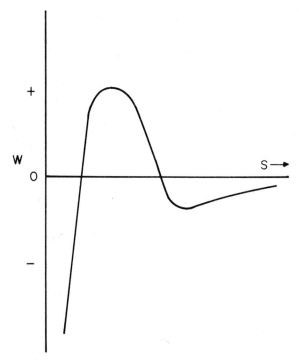

Fig. 4-7. An approximation of the behavior of the total energy of interaction W, between two macroscopic spheres as a function of separation distance S (schematic). $W = W_E + W_A$; W_E (repulsive) = potential energy due to electrical forces; W_A (attractive) = potential energy due to van der Waals' forces.

maximum in Fig. 4-7 signifies an activation energy. Particles will not coagulate if they cannot overcome this activation energy.

How do we calculate the activation energy? Let us investigate the situation at small distances ($R \simeq 2a$), where the particles are close enough that we can use the approximation from (4-3) and (4-20):

$$W \simeq -\frac{A}{12}\frac{a}{S} + \frac{\epsilon a \zeta^2}{2} e^{-\kappa S} \qquad (4\text{-}22)$$

If we write $\kappa S = S/\lambda = \sigma$, then

$$W = -\frac{A}{12}\frac{\kappa a}{\sigma} + \frac{\epsilon a \zeta^2}{2} e^{-\sigma} \qquad (4\text{-}23)$$

This shows that the total potential energy (4-23) depends on the distance between the surfaces expressed in terms of the thickness of the ionic layer.

The quantity κa is the radius of the particle divided by the thickness of the ionic layer; both σ and κa are dimensionless. We see that the stability of colloids depends not only on the charge of the particles but also on the ions which surround the particle; e.g., κ is related to the concentration.

According to (4-23), we have $dW/d\sigma = 0$ at the maximum of the curve from a plot of W versus σ. Thus

$$-\frac{\epsilon a \zeta^2}{2} e^{-\sigma} + \frac{A}{12} \frac{\kappa a}{\sigma^2} = 0 \qquad \text{or} \qquad \sigma^2 e^{-\sigma} = \frac{A}{6} \frac{1}{\epsilon \lambda \zeta^2} \qquad (4\text{-}24)$$

If $A/6\epsilon\lambda\zeta^2$ is relatively small, there will be no maximum in the W versus σ plot, and so there is no activation energy. On the other hand, if $A/6\epsilon\lambda\zeta^2$ is equal to $\sigma^2 e^{-\sigma}$, (4-24), there is an upper limit for $A/6\epsilon\lambda\zeta^2$. We can determine this upper limit by considering a plot of $\sigma^2 e^{-\sigma}$ versus σ as shown in Fig. 4-8. The maximum appears at $2\sigma e^{-\sigma} - \sigma^2 e^{-\sigma} = 0$, or $\sigma = 2$. At $\sigma = 2$, $\sigma^2 e^{-\sigma}$ has a value of $4/e^2$. Therefore, for a maximum (and also a minimum) to exist in the W versus σ (or S) plot, we must have

$$\frac{A}{6\epsilon\lambda\zeta^2} < \frac{4}{e^2} \qquad \text{or} \qquad \zeta^2 > \frac{e^2 A}{24\epsilon\lambda} \qquad (4\text{-}25)$$

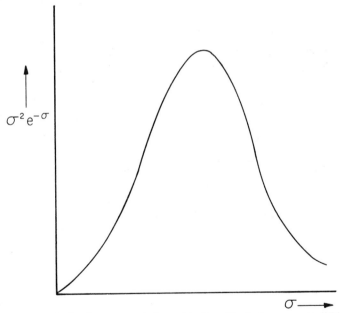

Fig. 4-8. Plot of $\sigma^2 e^{-\sigma}$ versus σ (schematic). See M. J. Sparnaay in "Rheology of Emulsions" (P. Sherman, ed.), Macmillan, New York, 1963, page 30, for further discussions.

With a millimolar aqueous solution of a uni-univalent electrolyte, $A \simeq 10^{-2}$ erg, $\epsilon \simeq 80$, and $\lambda \simeq 100$ A, so that

$$\zeta^2 > 0.39 \times 10^{-8} \text{ esu}$$

Thus we finally get $\zeta > 0.63 \times 10^{-4}$ esu, which is equal to 19 mv. If the effect of the electric charge is small, ζ^2 may be small enough so that $A/6\epsilon\lambda\zeta^2$ is greater than the maximum of the $\sigma^2 e^{-\sigma}$ versus σ plot. As a result, there is no maximum or minimum in the W versus σ plot. However, as the effect of the electric charge gets bigger, ζ^2 becomes bigger, and $A/6\epsilon\lambda\zeta^2$ eventually becomes smaller than the maximum of the $\sigma^2 e^{-\sigma}$ versus σ curve. When $A/6\epsilon\lambda\zeta^2 = 4/e^2$, the zeta potential is at its critical value:

$$\zeta_{\text{crit}} = \frac{e}{2}\left(\frac{A}{6\epsilon\lambda}\right)^{1/2} \tag{4-26}$$

Suppose ζ is a good deal larger than ζ_{crit}; then $A/6\epsilon\lambda\zeta^2$ intersects the $\sigma^2 e^{-\sigma}$ versus σ curve at two points which correspond to a maximum and a minimum in the energy curve. The distance between the maximum and the minimum increases with increasing ζ.

The minimum of the energy curve should indicate some arrangements of particles at relatively large distances from our arbitrarily selected central particle. We are, however, more interested in the maximum, which characterizes the activation energy. In our case, with a 1 mM aqueous solution of a uni-univalent electrolyte, the particle has to have an energy of at least 19 mv.

From (4-24),

$$e^{-\sigma_0} = \frac{A}{6}\frac{1}{\epsilon\lambda\zeta^2}\frac{1}{\sigma_0^2} \tag{4-27}$$

The subscript 0 signifies the maximum or minimum in the corresponding energy curve. With (4-27) and (4-23) we find

$$W_0 = \frac{A}{12}\frac{\kappa a}{\sigma_0}\left(\frac{1}{\sigma_0} - 1\right) \tag{4-28}$$

For $\zeta \gg \zeta_{\text{crit}}$, $\sigma_0 \ll 1$; then (4-27) reduces to

$$\sigma_0^2 \simeq \frac{A}{6}\frac{1}{\epsilon\lambda\zeta^2}$$

and

$$W_0 \simeq \frac{A}{12}\frac{\kappa a}{\sigma_0^2} = \frac{\epsilon a\zeta^2}{2}$$

For example, if we take $a = 0.5$ μ, $\epsilon = 80$, and $\zeta = 100$ mv,[†]

$$W_0 \simeq 40 \cdot \frac{10^{-4}}{2} \left(\frac{0.1}{300}\right)^2 = 2.2 \times 10^{-10} \text{ erg}$$

When compared with thermal energy kT at room temperature, we find

$$\frac{W_0}{kT} \simeq \frac{1}{2} \times 10^4$$

This means that when the zeta potential is much greater than its critical value, the activation energy W_0 is about 5000 times greater than the thermal energy.

B. Coagulation

We have seen that the stability of colloids depends on the magnitude of the activation energy. From the curves representing the total potential energy of interaction, the criterion for the stability of colloids can be derived. If the maximum is not very pronounced, the particles can come together relatively easily and there will be coagulation. The question is: How quickly will the coagulation take place? In other words, how does the time of coagulation depend on the activation energy which the particles have to overcome before they hit each other? The particles are in Brownian motion and have energies distributed according to Maxwell's equation. Hence there are always some particles which have a very big kinetic energy, big enough to overcome the activation energy, which is finite. As a result, these particles can hit each other, and coagulation takes place. Our first remark is that a colloid solution is never stable. The question then is: How long will it last before an appreciable number of particles coagulate? Or, what is the coagulation time? For example, we can ask how long we have to wait for half of the particles to come together as double particles. The calculation of coagulation time was first discussed by Smoluchowski (9) in connection with the rapid coagulation of gold particles. One pertinent question is: How many particles hit each other in 1 sec?

The idea is that a certain percentage of the single particles will hit each other and form double particles, which in turn may hit other single particles and form threefold particles, etc. After a certain amount of time, there is a distribution of double, threefold, fourfold, etc., particles. Smoluchowski solved the distribution problem with the assumptions that (1) there is no interaction between the particles, and (2) if two particles hit

[†] 1 esu = 300 volts.

each other, they stick. In essence, the encounter of two particles is treated as a diffusion problem.

Suppose we take an arbitrarily fixed sphere of radius a. Then we make around this sphere another sphere with a radius of $2a$, as shown in Fig. 4-9.

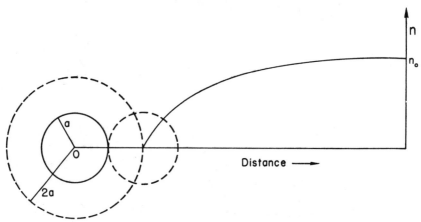

Fig. 4-9. Diffusion of particles at large distances to a hole with radius $2a$, taking into account the arbitrarily fixed sphere at the center of the hole.

The surface of the sphere with radius $2a$ is the superposition of the centers of other spheres which hit the arbitrarily fixed sphere. The particles are in Brownian motion. Let n_0 be the number of particles per cubic centimeter at a large distance from the center of the fixed sphere. Figure 4-9 is an illustration for the diffusion of particles at large distances to a hole with radius $2a$, taking into account the arbitrarily fixed sphere at the center of the hole. We want to calculate how many particles per second reach the central particle.

In our calculation we shall include a potential energy of interaction between two particles, $W(R)$. The force on each of the particles, $-\partial W/\partial R$, produces a velocity v, according to the relation $f = -\partial W/\partial R = \rho_v v$, where ρ_v is a friction constant. The current J, defined as the number of particles per second going through a unit cross section, is built up by two influences: (1) diffusion under the influence of a concentration gradient, and (2) displacement caused by the interaction of the particles:

$$J = 4\pi R^2 \left(-D\frac{\partial n}{\partial R} - \frac{1}{\rho_v}\frac{\partial W}{\partial R}n \right) \qquad (4\text{-}29)$$

Here $\partial n/\partial R$ is the concentration gradient and D is the diffusion constant.

In a stationary state, J is a constant. The mathematical details of (4-29) will not be discussed here, but can be found elsewhere (*10*). Now we have a differential equation for the number of particles as a function of the distance. We shall introduce in this equation an evaluation of the diffusion coefficient D. Einstein (*11*) has shown that diffusion can be looked at in two different ways. First, diffusion is directly connected with the Brownian motion of the solute particles: $D = \overline{\Delta^2}/2\tau$, where Δ is an irregular displacement, during time τ, of a particle in Brownian motion, and $\overline{\Delta^2}$ is the average square of a number of such displacements. Second, $D\rho_v = kT$. The reader may again consult standard texts (*12*) for the derivation of $D\rho_v = kT$. In our problem we should take into account the fact that the central particle is not really fixed. This means that the diffusion effect between two particles is increased by a factor of 2, and also that the relative displacement under the influence of the interaction forces is doubled. So, with the Brownian movement of the central particle taken into account, (4-29) has the form

$$\frac{dn}{dR} + \frac{n}{kT}\frac{dW}{dR} = \frac{\rho_v J}{8\pi kT}\frac{1}{R^2} \tag{4-30}$$

Suppose we assume a Boltzmann distribution so that $n = Ae^{-W/kT}$. Then

$$\frac{dA}{dR}e^{-W/kT} = -\frac{\rho_v J}{8\pi kT}\frac{1}{R^2}$$

The boundary conditions are

$$n = 0 \qquad \text{when} \qquad R = 2a$$
$$n = n_0 \qquad \text{and} \qquad W = 0 \qquad \text{when} \qquad R = \infty$$

Thus

$$\int_{n=0}^{n=n_0} dA = -\frac{\rho_v J}{8\pi kT}\int_{R=2a}^{R=\infty} e^{W/kT}\frac{dR}{R^2}$$

or

$$n_0 = -\frac{\rho_v J}{8\pi kT}\int_{2a}^{\infty} e^{W/kT}\frac{dR}{R^2}$$

and

$$-J = \frac{8\pi kT}{\rho_v}n_0\frac{1}{\int_{2a}^{\infty} e^{W/kT}(dR/R^2)} \tag{4-31}$$

Stoke's law† states that the frictional force f due to viscosity acting on a

---

† See a standard text such as J. R. Partington, *An Advanced Treatise on Physical Chemistry*, Vol. II, Longmans, Green, London, 1955, p. 85.

small sphere of radius a falling through a large (theoretically infinite) bulk of liquid of viscosity η with a velocity v is

$$f = 6\pi\eta va$$

We also know that the minimum distance between the centers of two particles is twice their radius, since $n = 0$ for $R = 2a$. Thus we can write

$$-J = \frac{8\pi akTn_0}{6\pi\eta a} \frac{1}{a \int_{2a}^{\infty} e^{W/kT} (dR/R^2)}$$

$$= \frac{8}{3} \frac{kT}{\eta} n_0 \frac{1}{2a \int_{2a}^{\infty} e^{W/kT} (dR/R^2)}$$

or

$$-J = \frac{1}{\theta^*} \frac{1}{q} = \frac{1}{\theta} \tag{4-32}$$

with $\theta^* = (3\eta/8kT)(1/n_0)$ and $q = 2a \int_{2a}^{\infty} e^{W/kT}(dR/R^2)$. Here $-J$ represents the number of collisions against one particle in 1 sec and is a direct measure of the flocculation velocity. The quantity θ represents the time in which the number of particles is halved, taking into account collisions of single particles as well as double, threefold, and other secondary particles. When $W = 0$, i.e., when there is no interaction between the particles (except a very steep attraction when the particles touch each other), $q = 1$ and θ reduces to the "ideal" coagulation time, θ^*. To get an idea of the magnitudes involved, let us take, as an example, a solution with a viscosity of 0.01 poise at room temperature. This gives

$$\theta^* \sim \frac{3 \times 0.01}{8 \times 4 \times 10^{-14}n_0} \sim \frac{10^{11}}{n_0} \tag{4-33}$$

For colloids, $10^{10} < n_0 < 10^{14}$ cc^{-1}, and so

$$10 > \theta^* > 10^{-3} \text{ sec}$$

This "ideal" coagulation time θ^* gives a measure for rapid coagulation and is independent of particle size. When there is an interaction energy, W, the velocity of coagulation is diminished by the factor

$$q = 2a \int_{2a}^{\infty} e^{W/kT} \frac{dR}{R^2} \tag{4-34}$$

The factor q is a number which depends on the magnitude of the potential energy of interaction. If the particles repel each other over a certain distance, W is positive, $e^{W/kT}$ will be a large factor as soon as W/kT is relatively greater than 1, and q will be significant. The real coagulation time, θ, is $q\theta^*$. At large distances, van der Waals' attraction is important; then as the separation distance becomes smaller, the electrical repulsion takes over; and finally van der Waals' attraction becomes more important again. If the particles want to touch each other, they have to overcome the activation energy, which is represented by the maximum of the W versus S plot (Fig. 4-7). The activation energy is a function of S. On differentiating (4-23) with respect to S, we obtain

$$W' = \frac{\epsilon a \zeta^2}{2} \kappa e^{-\kappa s} + \frac{A}{12} \frac{a}{S^2}$$

and

$$W'' = \frac{\epsilon a \zeta^2}{2} \kappa^2 e^{-\kappa s} - \frac{A}{6} \frac{a}{S^3}$$

Recall that

$$W_0 = \frac{A}{12} \frac{a}{S_0} \left(\frac{1}{\kappa S_0} - 1 \right)$$

from (4-28) and

$$e^{-\kappa S_0} = \frac{A}{6} \frac{1}{\epsilon \kappa \zeta^2} \frac{1}{S_0^2}$$

from (4-27). At $S = S_0$, we have

$$W_0'' = -\frac{A}{6} \frac{a}{S_0} \left(\frac{1}{S_0^2} - \frac{\kappa}{2S_0} \right)$$

and can develop W around W_0 so that

$$W = W_0 + \frac{1}{2} W_0''(S - S_0) + \cdots$$

$$= \frac{A}{12} \frac{a}{S_0} \left(\frac{1}{\kappa S_0} - 1 \right) - \frac{A}{12} \frac{a}{S_0} \left(\frac{1}{S_0^2} - \frac{\kappa}{2S_0} \right)(S - S_0)^2 + \cdots \quad (4\text{-}35)$$

and

$$e^{W/kT} = \exp\left[\frac{1}{kT} \left(W_0 + \frac{1}{2} W_0'' x^2 + \cdots \right) \right] \quad (4\text{-}36)$$

with $x = S - S_0$. Thus

$$q = 2a \int_{2a}^{\infty} e^{W/kT} \frac{dR}{R^2}$$

$$\simeq \frac{1}{2a} \int_0^{\infty} e^{W/kT} \, dS \qquad \text{for } R \simeq 2a \qquad (4\text{-}37)$$

Substituting (4-35) and (4-36) in the expression for q when S is small, we find

$$q \simeq \frac{1}{2a} \exp\left[\frac{A}{12kT}\frac{a}{S_0}\left(\frac{1}{\kappa S_0} - 1\right)\right] \int_0^{\infty} \exp\left[\frac{-A}{12kT}\frac{a}{S_0}\left(\frac{1}{S_0^2} - \frac{\kappa}{2S_0}\right)x^2\right] dx$$

$$= \frac{S_0}{2a}\left\{\frac{\pi}{(A/12kT)(a/S_0)[1 - (\kappa S_0/2)]}\right\}^{1/2} \exp\left[\frac{A}{12kT}\frac{a}{S_0}\left(\frac{1}{\kappa S_0} - 1\right)\right]$$

$$(4\text{-}38)$$

The truncation on (4-35) after the second term

$$W = W_0 + \tfrac{1}{2}W_0''(S - S_0)^2$$

is a good approximation, since the tail of the curve is unimportant. It should be emphasized that we may change the coagulation time exponentially from a change in the zeta potential.

REFERENCES

1. H. Kallman and M. Willstatter, *Naturwiss.*, **20**, 952 (1932).
2. E. J. W. Verwey and J. Th. G. Overbeek, *Theory of the Stability of Lyophobic Colloids*, Elsevier, Amsterdam, 1948.
3. J. H. de Boer, *Trans. Faraday Soc.*, **32**, 10 (1936).
4. H. C. Hamaker, *Rec. Trav. Chim.*, **55**, 1015 (1936); **56**, 3 (1937); *Physica*, **4**, 1058 (1937).
5. F. London and M. Polányi, *Naturwiss.*, **18**, 1099 (1930).
6. I. Langmuir, *J. Chem. Phys.*, **6**, 893 (1938).
7. P. Bergmann, P. Löw-Beer, and H. Zocher, *Z. Physik. Chem. (Leipzig)*, **A181**, 301 (1938).
8. B. V. Derjaguin, *Trans. Faraday Soc.*, **36**, 203 (1940).
9. M. V. Smoluchowski, *Physik. Z.*, **17**, 557, 585 (1916); *Z. Phys. Chem. (Leipzig)*, **92**, 129 (1917).
10. E. J. W. Verwey and J. Th. G. Overbeek, *Theory of the Stability of Lyophobic Colloids*, Elsevier, Amsterdam, 1948, Chap. XII.
11. A. Einstein, *Ann. Physik Chem.*, **17**, 132, 549 (1905).
12. A. Prock and G. McConkey, *Topics in Chemical Physics*, Elsevier, Amsterdam, 1962.

MODERNIZATION OF
LONDON'S INTERACTION THEORY

5-1. THEORY

London's theory, according to which the interaction energy between two atoms is inversely proportional to the sixth power of their separation distance, has been derived with the assumption that the interaction between atoms is purely electrostatic in nature. The calculation becomes inadequate for distances of the order of a few thousand angstroms because the instantaneous electrical moment varies in time with a frequency which has a magnitude corresponding to the frequency characteristic for the ionization energy of the atom (*1*). Furthermore, the theory is approximate because the electric field coming from an atom is considered in its first approximation to be the field of a dipole. The second approximation holds only for large distances, where the effects of higher poles are negligible.

In 1946–1948 Casimir and Polder performed a rather involved calculation in which the effect of the finite velocity of propagation of light was taken into account (*2*). The result was obtained by making some calculations in which the finite interaction energy appears to come from subtracting one infinity from another infinity. They obtained for the interaction energy of two atoms,

$$\varepsilon = -\frac{\alpha^2}{r^6}\frac{3}{4}\frac{hc}{\lambda_{\text{ion}}} \qquad \text{for short distances} \qquad (5\text{-}1)$$

$$\varepsilon = -\frac{\alpha^2}{r^6}\frac{23}{8\pi^2}\frac{hc}{r} \qquad \text{for large distances} \qquad (5\text{-}2)$$

Formula (5-1) is exactly the same as that obtained by London (3-15). We have only substituted c/λ_{ion} for v_{ion}, c being the velocity of light. In the second formula, which is valid for larger distances, the ionization wavelength λ_{ion} is replaced by the distance r, and in addition a different numerical constant has appeared.

The main point is that it now becomes evident that London's formula is applicable only for intermediate distances. If the distance becomes too small, the field can no longer be considered to be caused by an instantaneous dipole. If the distance is too large, the finite velocity of light has to be taken into account, so that the interaction energy decreases with the power 7 of the separation distance instead of the power 6. Equation (5-2) also shows that molecular interaction for large distances depends only on the polarizability. All other constants (h and c) are universal.

At about this time it also became clear that interaction energy for larger systems could not adequately be calculated by a simple summation over the interactions of the individual atoms. As the whole interaction is considered to be solely the result of an electromagnetic field, the distortions of this field by the presence of macroscopic bodies must be of importance. Simultaneously the idea came up that it should be possible to measure experimentally forces of attraction between two macroscopic parallel plates at separation distances of the order of the wavelength of visible light.

The first calculation of the force between two parallel perfect mirror flats is due to Casimir (3). The results are obtained by taking the usual London forces as a starting point and correcting for retardation effects. Casimir also derived those same formulas through the change of electromagnetic zero-point energy by means of classical electrodynamics (3). We shall derive the interaction between two perfectly conducting plates according to Casimir.

Let us consider a cubic cavity of volume L^3 with totally reflecting (perfectly conducting) walls (see Fig. 5-1). Into this cavity is introduced a second perfectly conducting square plate with side parallel to the xy face and at a short distance d from the bottom. Then, we have on top of each other one cavity with dimensions L, L, d, and the other with dimensions L, L, $L - d$. The free electrical vibrations in both cavities are calculated and their distribution over a frequency axis considered. The number of free vibrations per interval dv is proportional to $v^2 \, dv$. Each fundamental mode of frequency v is given a zero-point energy $hv/2$, and, finally, for a change of the distance from d to $d + dd$, the corresponding change of the total zero-point energy of both cavities is calculated. This seemingly straightforward derivation is indeed a very daring operation. In each cavity, the expression $\frac{1}{2} \sum hv$, where the summation extends over all possible resonance frequencies of the cavity, is divergent and devoid of physical meaning because we are dealing with infinite zero-point energies. However, the difference between these two infinite sums, $\frac{1}{2}(\sum hv)_{\mathrm{I}} - \frac{1}{2}(\sum hv)_{\mathrm{II}}$, has a finite value.

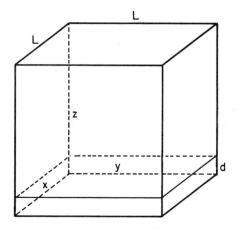

Fig. 5-1. A cubic cavity of volume L^3 with perfectly conducting walls.

The possible vibrations of a cavity, defined by $0 \leq x \leq L$, $0 \leq y \leq L$, $0 \leq z \leq d$, have wave numbers

$$k_x = \frac{\pi}{L} n_x \qquad k_y = \frac{\pi}{L} n_y \qquad k_z = \frac{\pi}{d} n_z \qquad (6\text{-}71)$$

where n_x, n_y, and n_z are positive integers, and $k = (k_x^2 + k_y^2 + k_z^2)^{1/2}$. There are two vibrations (standing waves) for every combination of n_x, n_y, and n_z, unless one of the n_i is zero, in which case there is only one.

For very large L, we may regard k_x and k_y as continuous variables. Thus we find

$$\frac{1}{2}\sum \hbar\omega = \hbar c \frac{L^2}{\pi^2} \iint_0^\infty \left[\frac{1}{2}(k_x^2 + k_y^2)^{1/2} + \sum_{n=1}^\infty \left(n^2 \frac{\pi^2}{d^2} + k_x^2 + k_y^2 \right)^{1/2} \right] dk_x\, dk_y$$

in which $\hbar = h/2\pi$ and $\omega\ (= 2\pi\nu)$ is the angular frequency. If we put $\kappa^2 = k_x^2 + k_y^2$, and introduce polar coordinates, we find

$$U = \frac{1}{2}\sum \hbar\omega = \hbar c \frac{L^2}{\pi^2} \frac{\pi}{2} \sum_{(0)1}^\infty \int_0^\infty \left(\kappa^2 + \frac{n^2\pi^2}{d^2} \right)^{1/2} \kappa\, d\kappa \qquad (5\text{-}3)$$

where the notation $(0)1$ indicates that the term with $n = 0$ has to be multiplied by $\frac{1}{2}$. Our interaction energy, E, is the energy U (5-3) minus U_∞. For large d the last summation may again be replaced by an integral, so that

$$E = \frac{\pi}{2} \hbar c \frac{L^2}{\pi^2} \left[\sum_{(0)1}^\infty \int_0^\infty \left(\kappa^2 + \frac{n^2\pi^2}{d^2} \right)^{1/2} \kappa\, d\kappa \right.$$
$$\left. - \iint_0^\infty \left(\kappa^2 + \frac{n^2\pi^2}{d^2} \right)^{1/2} \kappa\, d\kappa \left(\frac{d}{\pi} dk_z \right) \right] \qquad (5\text{-}4)$$

The integrals in (5-4) are infinite, so we need a convergence factor ϕ. Introducing the variable $d^2\kappa^2/\pi^2 = \alpha^2$, we have

$$E = \frac{\pi}{2} \hbar c \frac{L^2}{\pi^2} \left(\frac{\pi}{d} \right)^3 \left[\sum_{(0)1}^\infty \int_0^\infty \phi(\alpha^2 + n^2)^{1/2}\alpha\, d\alpha - \iint_0^\infty \phi(\alpha^2 + n^2)^{1/2}\alpha\, d\alpha\, dn \right]$$
$$= \frac{\pi}{2} \hbar c \frac{L^2}{\pi^2} \left(\frac{\pi}{d} \right)^3 \frac{1}{2} \left[\sum_{(0)1}^\infty M(n) - \int_0^\infty M(n)dn \right]$$

where $M(n) = \int_{w=n^2}^\infty w^{1/2}\phi(w)dw$ and $w = \alpha^2 + n^2$; ϕ is an appropriate function of w. Now we apply the Euler-Maclaurin formula:

$$\sum_{(0)1}^\infty M(n) - \int_0^\infty M(n)dn = -\frac{1}{12} M'(0) + \frac{1}{24 \times 30} M'''(0) + \cdots$$

where

$$M'(n) = -2n^2\phi(n^2) \qquad M'(0) = 0$$
$$M''(n) = -4n$$
$$M'''(n) = -4 \qquad\qquad M'''(0) = -4$$

This yields

$$E = -\frac{\pi}{2} \hbar c \frac{L^2}{\pi^2} \left(\frac{\pi}{d}\right)^3 \frac{1}{2} \frac{4}{720} = -hc \frac{\pi}{1440} \frac{L^2}{d^3} \tag{5-5}$$

Equation (5-5) holds as long as d is larger than the penetration depth of electromagnetic waves (order of magnitude of 0.1 μ). Thus Casimir comes to the conclusion that the force per square centimeter between two perfect mirrors at a distance d apart should be attractive and have the value

$$|F| = \frac{\pi}{480} \frac{hc}{d^4} \tag{5-6}$$

in which h is the Planck constant and c is the velocity of light. Note that no material constants appear. If the distance d is expressed in microns, the numerical result is

$$|F| = \frac{0.013}{d_\mu^4} \quad \text{dynes/cm}^2 \tag{5-7}$$

The force may be interpreted as a zero-point pressure of electromagnetic waves.

In 1954 Lifshitz (4) extended the calculation to the case of two plates with material properties. For perfect mirrors he confirms Casimir's formula. Moreover, he shows how to correct for finite conductivities of the mirrors. He also considers the case of two dielectric plates made of material with dielectric constant ϵ. In this case, he finds

$$|F| = \frac{\pi}{480} \frac{hc}{d^4} \left(\frac{\epsilon - 1}{\epsilon + 1}\right)^2 \phi(\epsilon) \tag{5-8}$$

where $\phi(\epsilon)$ is a function which he determined by a graphical method. It varies from $\phi = 1$ for $\epsilon = \infty$ to $\phi = 0.35$ for $\epsilon = 1$, as shown in Table 5-1.

TABLE 5-1

ϵ	$\dfrac{1}{\epsilon}$	$\phi(\epsilon)$	$\left(\dfrac{\epsilon - 1}{\epsilon + 1}\right)^2 \phi(\epsilon)$
∞	0	1	1
40	0.025	0.53	0.48
10	0.1	0.41	0.27
4	0.25	0.37	0.13
2	0.5	0.35	0.04
1	1	0.35	0

In general, it is necessary to determine the complex dielectric constant for the full range of frequencies before we can calculate the force.

Our main reason for discussing these results is that the force between plates should decrease with the fourth power of the distance instead of the third power, as predicted by the calculation of de Boer and Hamaker (Chapter 4). This fourth-power dependence is in essence a consequence of the finite velocity of propagation of the electromagnetic radiation, and it supersedes the classical calculations of de Boer and Hamaker using London's theory.

In addition to being affected by the distortion of electromagnetic field due to the presence of a dielectric medium, the energy between molecules should depend on temperature. Since molecules (or atoms) go to excited states at higher temperatures, the interaction between molecules (or atoms) at different temperatures will be different. The effect of temperature on the molecular forces of attraction between condensed bodies was calculated by Lifshitz (5). For the interaction between two metal plates he obtains

$$|F| = \frac{\pi}{480} \frac{hc}{d^4} \left[1 - \frac{48}{9} \left(\frac{dkT}{\hbar c} \right)^4 \right] \tag{5-9}$$

provided d is assumed to be small relative to $\hbar c / kT$, yet large when compared with the "wavelength," which is characteristic for metal. At room temperatures the correction term is small even when $d < 5\,\mu$. For a reverse limiting case of large values of $dkT/\hbar c$ we can write

$$|F| \simeq \frac{kT}{8\pi d^3} \left(\frac{\epsilon_s - 1}{\epsilon_s + 1} \right)^2 \tag{5-10}$$

where ϵ_s is the electrostatic value of the dielectric constant. Thus, at sufficiently large distances, the decrease of the molecular force is retarded and F follows the law of $1/d^3$ with the coefficient now depending on the temperature and on the electrostatic dielectric constant. Using fourth-order perturbation theory and dipole approximation, McLone and Power (6) found that (1) the interaction energy between two dissimilar nonionized molecules or atoms agrees with the London force at small separation distances, (2) the interaction energy for two molecules both in their ground state agrees with the modification of Casimir and Polder for separations large compared with the characteristic wavelengths, and (3) new effects appear at large distances when one of the molecules is in an excited state. The interaction energy depends on the orientation of the transition moment in the excited molecule. We refer the interested reader to the original paper (6) for details.

5-2. EXPERIMENTS ON VAN DER WAALS' ATTRACTION BETWEEN TWO PLATES

Measurements of molecular attractions between macroscopic objects have been reported by Derjaguin and Abrikosova; by Overbeek and Sparnaay; by Howe, Benton, and Puddington; by Kitchener and Prosser; and by others (7–16).

The main experiments were performed with glass or quartz plates or with metal plates. The last case was investigated by Sparnaay. The plates, made of steel or chromium, were brought to separation distances varying between 500 and 20,000 A. It was found that several difficulties could be encountered: (1) dust particles or other obstacles prevent free movements of the plates at short distances; (2) static electric charges, when situated in a given distribution, increase the attraction; and (3) potential effects occur when the two plates have different surface potentials and when electrical charges are able to go from one surface to the other. The electrostatic effects can be minimized for measurements between metal plates which are conductive. In case (3) the attractive force is inversely proportional to the square of the interplate distance. The force between two parallel plates was measured by the motion of the arm of a balance. The amplitude of this motion was measured by the change of capacity of a two-plate condenser of which one plate was moving with the arm of the balance. This change of capacity was measured by a beat-frequency method. Figure 5-2 shows the kind of plot obtained from measurements with chromium steel, chromium, and aluminum plates (16). The conclusion drawn from these experiments was that the measured force was what would be expected from Casimir's formula, (5-6). The force increased strongly with diminishing distance, and the increase was not in contradiction with the formula's exponent of 4 within the limits of error of the experiments.

Measurements with glass and quartz plates were started much earlier, probably because the distance between two transparent plates could be determined by merely observing Newton rings. The experimental results of the Russian investigators and those of the Utrecht School (Overbeek, Sparnaay, and others) did not coincide. However, in 1960 agreement was established in a paper by Black et al. (14) entitled "Measurements of Retarded van der Waals' Forces." The conclusion reached in this paper is

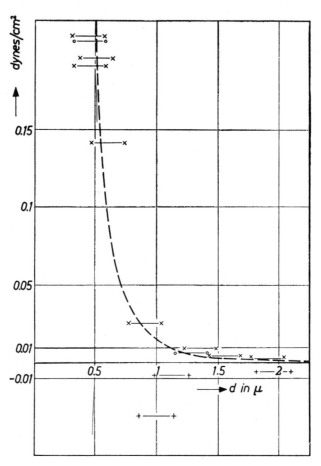

Fig. 5-2. Attractive forces between flat plates: x-x chromium steel, o-o chromium. Uncertainty of the determination of the distance between the plates is indicated by drawing horizontal lines instead of points. Any given measurement was often repeated. Some repulsions between aluminum plates are also given (*16*). Casimir's relation:
$$|F| = 0.013/d_\mu^4 \text{ dynes/cm}^2.$$

as follows: If the force per square centimeter between quartz plates is written in the form

$$|F| = \frac{B}{d_\mu^4} \qquad \text{dynes/cm}^2 \tag{5-11}$$

with the separation distance d_μ measured in microns, the value of the coefficient B derived from experiments is between 1×10^{-3} and 2×10^{-3}.

This means that molecular attraction between quartz plates is about 10 times smaller than it is between metal plates. The theoretical value of B could be computed from a Lifshitz formula if the dispersion curve for quartz were well known. We can calculate two approximate values for B from (5-8). The first value is obtained by taking for the refractive index of quartz a value of 1.46; this leads to $B = 0.6 \times 10^{-3}$. The second value is obtained by using a value of 3.75 for the dielectric constant; this leads to $B = 1.6 \times 10^{-3}$. There seems to be now a very satisfactory agreement not

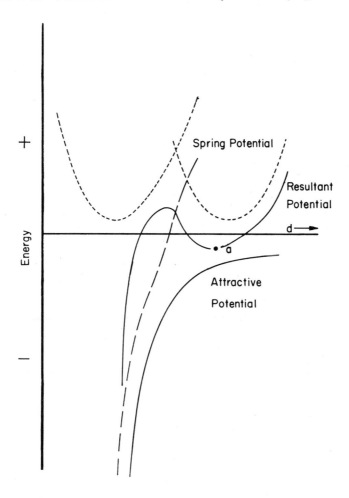

Fig. 5-3. Equilibrium between molecular attractions and spring "repulsion."

only between the different laboratories but also between experiment and theory.

It should be emphasized that the attractive force between plates becomes rather big for small separation distances. For example, if in Casimir's formula, (5-6), we insert for the distance d a value of 100 A (0.01 μ), the force per square centimeter between two plates is calculated to be 1.3 $\times$ 10^6 dynes. This means that there is an intrinsic limitation for each spring in direct measurements of molecular forces of attraction between plates by the balance method, because it is necessary to establish an equilibrium between the molecular attractions and the force of the spring which keeps the plates apart. The equilibrium position is sketched in Fig. 5-3 as point a in the curve (solid line), representing the resultant potential. At distances smaller than a certain minimum, r_m, stable equilibrium conditions no longer exist (dashed line). Thus measurements cannot be made at distances smaller than r_m using that particular spring.

REFERENCES

1. E. J. W. Verwey and J. Th. G. Overbeek, *Theory of the Stability of Lyophobic Colloids*, Elsevier, Amsterdam, 1948, p. 104.

2. H. B. G. Casimir and D. Polder, *Nature*, **158**, 787 (1946); *Phys. Rev.*, **73**, 360 (1948).

3. H. B. G. Casimir, *Konkinkl. Ned. Akad. Wetenschap. Proc.*, **51**, 793 (1948); first presented at the "Colloque sur la théorie de la liaison chemique," Paris, April 1948.

4. E. M. Lifschitz, *Dokl. Akad. Nauk SSSR*, **97**, 643 (1954); *J. Exptl. Theoret. Phys. (USSR)*, **29**, 94 (1955).

5. E. M. Lifshitz, *Dokl. Akad. Nauk SSSR*, **100**, 879 (1955).

6. R. R. McLone and E. A. Power, *Proc. Roy. Soc. (London)*, **A286**, 573 (1965).

7. J. Th. G. Overbeek and M. J. Sparnaay, *Konkinkl. Ned. Akad. Wetenschap. Proc.*, **54**, 387 (1951); *J. Colloid Sci.*, **7**, 343 (1952); *Discussions Faraday Soc.*, **18**, 12 (1954).

8. M. J. Sparnaay, Thesis, Utrecht, 1952; *Nature*, **180**, 334 (1957); *Physica*, **24**, 751 (1958).

9. B. V. Derjaguin and I. I. Abrikosova, *Zh. Eksptl. Teoret. Fiz.*, **21**, 945 (1951); *Dokl. Akad. Nauk SSSR*, **90**, 1055 (1952); *Discussions Faraday Soc.*, **18**, 24 (1954); *Zh. Eksptl. Teoret. Fiz.*, **30**, 993 (1956); **31**, 3 (1956); *Soviet Phys. JETP (English Transl.)*, **3**, 819 (1957); **4**, 2 (1957); *Dokl. Akad. Nauk SSSR*, **108**, 214 (1956); *Soviet Phys. "Doklady" (English Transl.)*, **1**, 280 (1956); *Proc. Intern. Congr. Surface Activity*, *2nd, London*, **3**, 398 (1957); *Phys. Chem. Solids*, **5**, 1 (1958).

10. B. V. Derjaguin, I. I. Abrikosova, and E. M. Lifshitz, *Quart. Rev. (London)*, **10**, 295 (1956).

11. P. G. Howe, D. P. Benton, and I. E. Puddington, *Can. J. Chem.*, **33**, 1375 (1955).

12. J. A. Kitchener and A. P. Prosser, *Nature*, **178**, 1339 (1956); *Proc. Roy. Soc. (London)*, **A242**, 403 (1957).

13. J. G. V. de Jongh, Thesis, Utrecht, 1958.
14. W. Black, J. G. V. de Jongh, J. Th. G. Overbeek, and M. J. Sparnaay, *Trans. Faraday Soc.*, **56**, 1597 (1960).
15. M. J. Sparnaay and P. W. J. Jochems, *Proc. Intern. Congr. Surface Activity*, *3rd*, Cologne, **2**, Sec. B, 1960.
16. M. J. Sparnaay, *Physica*, **24**, 762, Fig. 4 (1958).

CHAPTER **6**

ELECTROMAGNETIC
SCATTERING

6-1. PARTICLE SCATTERING

Electromagnetic scattering can tell us about the geometry of macromolecules. In principle, the scattering behavior is also related to molecular interactions. We shall start with geometry, which includes the dimension and shape of particles. Both visible light and X rays are electromagnetic waves, and so, from a theoretical viewpoint, they obey the same Maxwell equations. Their main difference, as far as scattering is concerned, is that they serve as "measuring sticks" of different magnitudes, because visible light has a wavelength a few thousand times greater than that of X rays.

The general problem of scattering came up a long time ago when in 1871 Rayleigh (1) treated light as mechanical vibrations, and based his explanation on the old elastic theory of light. He found that the amount of scattering should be proportional to the reciprocal fourth power of the wavelength. In 1881 Rayleigh (2) deduced the same results from the Maxwell electromagnetic wave theory. This reciprocal fourth-power dependence of the wavelength has become known as the *Rayleigh law*. A demonstration of this law is seen in the blue color of the sky. How strong is this scattering? We may demonstrate it by passing monochromatic light of various wavelengths through pure benzene, as shown in Fig. 6-1. The distance indicates the path length over which the light must travel before it loses half of its primary intensity by scattering. Note that, in pure benzene, the half distance for red light is about 110 m, whereas it is about 40 m for blue light. This behavior is in agreement with the Rayleigh law, which shows stronger scattering as the wavelength gets shorter.

One approach to the scattering problem is to make a detailed calculation of the electromagnetic field surrounding a particle in order to derive the loss of primary light due to its radiation. However, the calculation becomes very difficult whenever the particles are no longer far apart, as in the case of a pure liquid where the molecules are close to each other and interaction between the molecules exists. This seemingly difficult problem was treated by Einstein (*3*). He assumed the effect of molecular inhomogeneities on electromagnetic waves to be due to local thermal fluctuations in the density of the medium, which in a first approximation was considered to be perfectly homogeneous. The scattering formula from Einstein's fluctuation theory will be the background of our application of light scattering to the study of molecular interactions.

We recall the electrostatic formula

$$\boldsymbol{\mu} = \alpha\mathbf{F} \tag{6-1}$$

in which $\boldsymbol{\mu}$ is the induced dipole moment, α is the polarizability, and $\mathbf{F}$ is the applied electric field. The displacement vector $\mathbf{D}$ is connected to the applied electric field by an experimental relationship $\mathbf{D} = \epsilon\mathbf{F}$, where

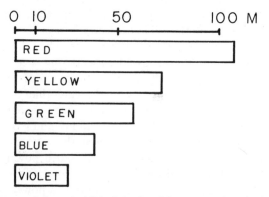

Fig. 6-1. Transmission of visible light for different wavelengths in benzene.

ϵ is the dielectric constant. From electrostatics we know that $\mathbf{D} = \mathbf{F} + 4\pi\mathbf{P}$, where $\mathbf{P}$ is the polarization per unit volume. Thus $\epsilon = 1 + 4\pi P/F$. Since $\epsilon = \varkappa^2$, and by definition $P = n\mu$, we obtain the familiar formula

$$\varkappa^2 - 1 = 4\pi n\alpha \qquad (3\text{-}2)$$

If $\varkappa$ is close to 1, so that $\varkappa^2 - 1 \simeq 2(\varkappa - 1)$, then

$$\varkappa - 1 = 2\pi n\alpha \qquad (6\text{-}2)$$

Equation (3-2) or (6-2) gives us a convenient and practical method for calculating the polarizability from refractive-index measurements.

A. Maxwell's Equations

The Maxwell equations are a set of partial differential equations describing the sources and relationships of the electromagnetic field vectors. We shall give a general outline of Maxwell's electromagnetic wave theory because of its fundamental importance. Let us first consider the results of several significant experiments which are represented as physical laws. For simplicity, we shall assume that the magnetic permeability is unity and that the dielectric constant ϵ is constant.

1. Faraday's Law of Electromagnetic Induction

Electromagnetic induction implies the creation of an electric field $\mathbf{E}$ by a time-varying magnetic field $\mathbf{H}$.

$$\oint_C \mathbf{E} \cdot d\mathbf{s} \propto \frac{\partial}{\partial t}(\text{flux}) \propto \int_{S_0} -\frac{\partial \mathbf{H}}{\partial t} \cdot \mathbf{n}\, dS$$

where C is any fixed, closed path of integration which is the boundary of the surface S_0; $\mathbf{n}$ is a unit vector normal to S_0; and $d\mathbf{s}$ and dS are elements of length and surface, respectively. We can write

$$\frac{\oint_C \mathbf{E} \cdot d\mathbf{s}}{\text{area}} \propto \frac{\partial}{\partial t}\frac{\text{flux}}{\text{area}} \propto -\frac{\partial}{\partial t}\mathbf{H}$$

with $\mathbf{H} = -\text{flux/area}$. As area approaches zero, we obtain a relationship known as Faraday's law:

$$\text{curl } \mathbf{E} = -\frac{1}{c}\frac{\partial \mathbf{H}}{\partial t} \qquad (6\text{-}3)$$

where c is the velocity of an electromagnetic wave in vacuum.

2. Ampere's Law

Ampere's law deals with the production of a magnetic field by an electric current:

$$\oint_C \mathbf{H} \cdot d\mathbf{s} \propto I$$

where I is net current which passes through any surface bounded by the closed path of integration C.

$$\frac{\oint_C \mathbf{H} \cdot d\mathbf{s}}{\text{area}} \propto \frac{I}{\text{area}} \propto J$$

where $J\ (= I/\text{area})$ is the current density due to free charge only. As area approaches zero, we obtain

$$\text{curl } \mathbf{H} = 4\pi \mathbf{J} \tag{6-4}$$

3. Lines of Magnetic Force

Lines of magnetic force have to be closed, since free magnetic charges do not exist. Thus we have

$$\text{div } \mathbf{H} = 0 \tag{6-5}$$

which signifies the absence of magnetic poles.

4. Gauss' Law

This is expressed mathematically as

$$\text{div}(\epsilon \mathbf{E}) = 4\pi \rho \tag{6-6}$$

where ρ is the charge density. Equation (6-6) signifies the presence of electric poles. The quantities have been written in cgs units.

In addition to these four experimental laws, we must consider the equation of continuity denoting the conservation of electric charges:

$$\text{div } \mathbf{J} + \frac{1}{c}\frac{\partial \rho}{\partial t} = 0 \tag{6-7}$$

Equation (6-7) implies that (6-4) is invalid in nonsteady states. Let us see why this is so and what Maxwell did to make (6-3) and (6-4) consistent. We recall the general mathematical relations

$$\text{div curl } \mathbf{A} = 0 \qquad \text{curl grad } \phi = 0$$

in which $\mathbf{A}$ is any vector and ϕ any scalar. With this, we get from (6-4),

$$\text{div curl } \mathbf{H} = 4\pi \, \text{div } \mathbf{J} = 0$$

which is impossible if there is a change in charge density with time as shown in (6-7). Therefore we may propose

$$\text{div curl } \mathbf{H} = \text{div } 4\pi \mathbf{J} + \text{div } 4\pi \mathbf{X} \tag{6-8}$$

where, in accordance with (6-7), $\text{div } \mathbf{X} = (1/c)(\partial\rho/\partial t)$. From (6-6) we may write

$$\text{div} \frac{\partial}{\partial t}(\epsilon\mathbf{E}) = 4\pi \frac{\partial\rho}{\partial t} \tag{6-9}$$

So

$$\frac{1}{c}\frac{\partial}{\partial t}(\epsilon\mathbf{E}) = 4\pi\mathbf{X} \tag{6-10}$$

Thus we finally obtain, in place of (6-4),

$$\text{curl } \mathbf{H} - \frac{\epsilon}{c}\frac{\partial}{\partial t}\mathbf{E} = 4\pi\mathbf{J}$$

In summary, the Maxwell equations with unit magnetic permeability and constant dielectric constant are

$$(1) \quad \text{curl } \mathbf{E} + \frac{1}{c}\frac{\partial\mathbf{H}}{\partial t} = 0$$

$$(2) \quad \text{curl } \mathbf{H} - \frac{\epsilon}{c}\frac{\partial\mathbf{E}}{\partial t} = 4\pi\mathbf{J}$$

$$(3) \quad \text{div } \mathbf{H} = 0$$

$$(4) \quad \text{div } \mathbf{E} = \frac{4\pi\rho}{\epsilon}$$

In a dielectric medium, we further assume that $\mathbf{J} = 0$ and $\rho = 0$. Then the Maxwell equations have the form

$$\frac{1}{c}\frac{\partial\mathbf{H}}{\partial t} = -\text{curl } \mathbf{E} \qquad \frac{\epsilon}{c}\frac{\partial\mathbf{E}}{\partial t} = \text{curl } \mathbf{H} \tag{6-11}$$

$$\text{div } \mathbf{H} = 0 \qquad \text{div}(\epsilon\mathbf{E}) = 0$$

These equations are the four basic relations which form the background of our light-scattering theory.

There is, of course, a vector potential which can be designated **A**. Since div curl $\mathbf{A} = 0$ and div $\mathbf{H} = 0$, we may write

$$\mathbf{H} = \text{curl } \mathbf{A}$$

This **A** is any vector which satisfies the conditions of div curl **A** $= 0$ and div **H** $= 0$, and is not unique. When curl **A** is substituted in the other three Maxwell equations (6-11), and a scalar quantity, $-$ grad ϕ, is used to represent the vector whose curl vanishes everywhere, we get, finally,†

$$\mathbf{E} = - \text{ grad } \phi - \frac{1}{c} \frac{\partial \mathbf{A}}{\partial t} \tag{6-12}$$

$$\text{div } \mathbf{A} = - \frac{\epsilon}{c} \frac{\partial \phi}{\partial t} \tag{6-13}$$

$$\text{curl curl } \mathbf{A} - \text{grad div } \mathbf{A} + \frac{\epsilon}{c^2} \frac{\partial^2 \mathbf{A}}{\partial t^2} = 0 \tag{6-14}$$

$$\text{div grad } \phi - \frac{\epsilon}{c^2} \frac{\partial^2 \phi}{\partial t^2} = 0 \tag{6-15}$$

where ϕ is the scalar potential.

For sinusoidal waves, **E** and **H** are proportional to $e^{i\omega t}$. Then

$$\mathbf{E} = \mathbf{E}^* e^{i\omega t} \qquad \mathbf{H} = \mathbf{H}^* e^{i\omega t}$$

and the solutions of Maxwell's equations are cisoidal functions, so space and time coordinates can always be separated. Carrying out the calculation, we have

$$ik_0 \mathbf{H} = - \text{ curl } \mathbf{E} \qquad i\varkappa^2 k_0 \mathbf{E} = \text{curl } \mathbf{H}$$

$$\text{div } \mathbf{H} = 0 \qquad \text{div } \mathbf{E} = 0 \tag{6-16}$$

---

† We recall that in rectangular coordinates,

$$\text{div } \mathbf{A} = \frac{\partial A_x}{\partial x} + \frac{\partial A_y}{\partial y} + \frac{\partial A_z}{\partial z}$$

$$\text{grad } \phi = \frac{\partial \phi}{\partial x} \mathbf{i} + \frac{\partial \phi}{\partial y} \mathbf{j} + \frac{\partial \phi}{\partial z} \mathbf{k}$$

$$\text{curl } \mathbf{A} = \lim_{\text{area} \to 0} \frac{\oint \mathbf{A} \cdot d\mathbf{s}}{\text{area}}$$

$$= \begin{vmatrix} \mathbf{i} & \mathbf{j} & \mathbf{k} \\ \dfrac{\partial}{\partial x} & \dfrac{\partial}{\partial y} & \dfrac{\partial}{\partial z} \\ A_x & A_y & A_z \end{vmatrix}$$

A_i being the ith component of vector **A**.

where $k_0 = \omega/c = 2\pi/\lambda_0$, ω is the angular frequency, c is the velocity of light in a vacuum, λ_0 is the wavelength in a vacuum, and $\varkappa^2$ is the square of the refractive index, taken to be equivalent to the dielectric constant ϵ. The superscript * for **E** and **H** has been deleted. Furthermore, (6-14) and (6-15) have the simplified form

$$\text{div grad } \mathbf{A} + \varkappa^2 k_0^2 \mathbf{A} = 0 \qquad (6\text{-}14a)$$

$$\text{div grad } \phi + \varkappa^2 k_0^2 \phi = 0 \qquad (6\text{-}15a)$$

Since

$$\frac{\epsilon}{c^2} \frac{\partial^2}{\partial t^2} \equiv -\epsilon \frac{\omega^2}{c^2} = -\varkappa^2 k_0^2$$

and by definition curl $\mathbf{A} = \mathbf{H}$, we can write (6-14) in the following form:

$$\mathbf{E} = -ik_0 \left[\mathbf{A} + \frac{1}{\varkappa^2 k_0^2} \text{grad div } \mathbf{A} \right] \qquad (6\text{-}14b)$$

Consider a vector potential **A** such that

$$A_x = A_y = 0 \qquad \text{and} \qquad \mathbf{A} = A_z \mathbf{k} \qquad (6\text{-}17)$$

in which **k** is a unit vector pointing in the z direction in rectangular coordinates. Then from (6-14a) we find

$$\text{div grad } A_z + \varkappa^2 k_0^2 A_z = 0 \qquad (6\text{-}14c)$$

The symmetry of the condition (6-17) reduces (6-14c) in spherical coordinates to a function of r only:

$$\frac{1}{r^2} \frac{\partial}{\partial r} \left(r^2 \frac{\partial A_z}{\partial r} \right) + \varkappa^2 k_0^2 A_z = 0$$

The solution for this partial differential equation is

$$A_z = C \frac{e^{-i\varkappa k_0 r}}{r}$$

where the constant C may be evaluated by considering the case in which the wavelength is much greater than r. The final answer is

$$\mathbf{A} = ik_0 \mu \frac{e^{-i\varkappa k_0 r}}{r} \mathbf{k} \qquad (6\text{-}18)$$

To find the radiation field surrounding a small particle at large distances, we have merely to adjust the solution of Maxwell's equations in such a way that the radiation field at small distances is equal to the electrostatic field of one dipole vibrating with the frequency of light. Suppose we take the center of the dipole as the origin of a coordinate system, and choose the z axis to be in the direction of the dipole vector μ. We then have symmetry about the z axis and the radiation fields are

$$\mathbf{E} = -\mu k_0^2 \frac{e^{i(\omega t - \varkappa k_0 r)}}{r} \sin \vartheta \, \mathbf{i}_2 \tag{6-19}$$

$$\mathbf{H} = -\mu k_0^2 \varkappa \frac{e^{i(\omega t - \varkappa k_0 r)}}{r} \sin \vartheta \, \mathbf{i}_3 \tag{6-20}$$

where $\mathbf{i}_1$ and $\mathbf{i}_2$ are mutually perpendicular unit vectors that point in the directions of increasing r and ϑ, respectively, and $\mathbf{i}_1 \times \mathbf{i}_2 = \mathbf{i}_3$. The angle ϑ measures the latitude angle from the z axis. $\mathbf{E} = \mathbf{H} \equiv 0$ at both the south and the north poles, as shown in Fig. 6-2. The vectors $\mathbf{E}$ and $\mathbf{H}$ may also be

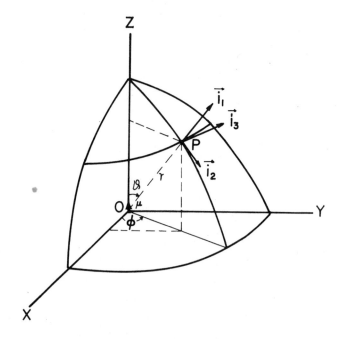

Fig. 6-2. Dipole μ oriented toward the z axis.

expressed in rectangular coordinates, using (6-14b) and the relation $\mathbf{H} =$ curl $\mathbf{A}$. Then we get for *large distances*,

$$\mathbf{H} = \begin{cases} k_0^2 \varkappa\mu \dfrac{e^{i(\omega t - \varkappa k_0 r)}}{r} \dfrac{y}{r} \mathbf{i} \\[2ex] -k_0^2 \varkappa\mu \dfrac{e^{i(\omega t - \varkappa k_0 r)}}{r} \dfrac{x}{r} \mathbf{j} \\[2ex] 0 \qquad\qquad \mathbf{k} \end{cases} \quad \mathbf{E} = \begin{cases} -k_0^2\mu \dfrac{e^{i(\omega t - \varkappa k_0 r)}}{r} \dfrac{xz}{r^2} \mathbf{i} \\[2ex] -k_0^2\mu \dfrac{e^{i(\omega t - \varkappa k_0 r)}}{r} \dfrac{yz}{r^2} \mathbf{j} \\[2ex] k_0^2\mu \dfrac{e^{i(\omega t - \varkappa k_0 r)}}{r} \left(1 - \dfrac{z^2}{r^2}\right) \mathbf{k} \end{cases}$$

where $\mathbf{i}$, $\mathbf{j}$, and $\mathbf{k}$ are the unit vectors in the x, y, and z directions of the rectangular coordinates. The electrical energy density u_e, and the magnetic energy density u_m, are

$$u_e = \frac{\epsilon E^2}{8\pi} \qquad u_m = \frac{\epsilon_m H^2}{8\pi}$$

with ϵ_m defined as the magnetic permeability. From (6-19) and (6-20) we get

$$u_e = u_m = \frac{\varkappa^2 k_0^4 \mu^2}{8\pi} \sin^2 \vartheta \frac{\cos^2(\omega t - \varkappa k_0 r)}{r^2} \tag{6-21}$$

B. Rayleigh Scattering

Consider an induced dipole of moment μ in the presence of an applied electrical field $F = F_0 e^{i\omega t}$. Then $\mu = \alpha F_0 e^{i\omega t}$, and the corresponding radiation field will be

$$\mathbf{E} = -k_0^2 \alpha F_0 \sin \vartheta \frac{e^{i(\omega t - \varkappa k_0 r)}}{r} \mathbf{i}_2$$

$$\mathbf{H} = \varkappa E \mathbf{i}_3$$

Thus we find the time average of the Poynting vector in gaussian units:

$$i_0 = \frac{c}{8\pi} |E_0|^2 \qquad i = \frac{c}{8\pi} |E|^2 \qquad \frac{i}{i_0} = \frac{k_0^4 \alpha^2 \sin^2 \vartheta}{r^2} \tag{6-22}$$

where i and i_0 are, respectively, the scattered and incident intensities. Equation (6-22) holds for polarized light. With N molecules in high dilution,

$$\frac{I}{I_0} = \frac{N k_0^4 \alpha^2 \sin^2 \vartheta}{r^2} \tag{6-23}$$

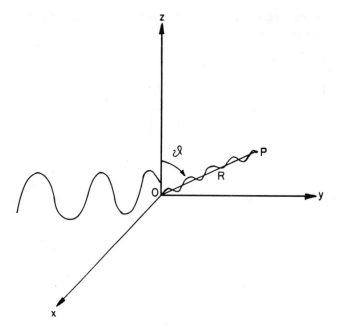

Fig. 6-3.

where I and I_0 are, respectively, the scattered and the incident intensities of N molecules. The scattered intensity is observed along the direction OR, which makes an angle ϑ with the z axis, as shown in Fig. 6-3. Integrating I over a big sphere, we find that the total energy loss per unit time is

$$\int_0^\pi I 2\pi r^2 \sin \vartheta \, d\vartheta$$

$$= \int_0^\pi I_0 \frac{N k_0^4 \alpha^2 \sin^2 \vartheta}{r^2} 2\pi r^2 \sin \vartheta \, d\vartheta$$

$$= 2\pi N k_0^4 \alpha^2 I_0 \int_0^\pi \sin^3 \vartheta \, d\vartheta$$

$$= 2\pi N k_0^4 \alpha^2 I_0 \int_{-1}^1 (1 - x^2) \, dx$$

$$= \frac{8\pi}{3} N k_0^4 \alpha^2 I_0 \qquad\qquad (6\text{-}24)$$

The turbidity τ is defined such that when the incident intensity I_0 of a light beam is decreased to I_t, the transmitted intensity, after it has traveled a distance d through the medium,

$$\frac{I_t}{I_0} = e^{-\tau d} \tag{6-25}$$

But (6-24) tells us that $dI = -(8\pi/3)nk_0^4\alpha^2 I_0 \, dx$, in which dI is the light loss after the incident beam has traveled through a thickness dx with n particles (dipoles) per cubic centimeter in the light path. Therefore,

$$\tau = \frac{8\pi}{3} nk_0^4\alpha^2$$

or

$$\tau = \frac{128\pi^5}{3} \frac{n\alpha^2}{\lambda_0^4} \tag{6-26}$$

The quantity τd is dimensionless, and τ has the dimensions of reciprocal length. Let us illustrate our result with an example: In the case of air at 1 atm and 0°C, $n = 2.7 \times 10^{19}$ molecules/cc, and $\varkappa - 1 = 2.92 \times 10^{-4}$ for the sodium D line, where $\lambda_0 = 5890$ A. Using (6-2) and (6-26) we get

$$\alpha = 1.72 \times 10^{-24} \text{ cc}$$

and

$$\tau = \frac{128\pi^5}{3} \frac{n\alpha^2}{\lambda_0^4} = 0.87 \times 10^{-7} \text{ cm}^{-1}$$

or

$$\frac{1}{\tau} = 1.15 \times 10^7 \text{ cm} = 115 \text{ km}$$

We have seen that for polarized light we have the scattered intensity proportional to $\sin^2 \vartheta$, ϑ being the angle between the direction of the vibrating dipole (z axis) and the direction of observation, OR, as shown in Fig. 6-3. However, in turbidity measurements unpolarized light is more commonly used. We then have the scattered intensity for unpolarized light proportional to

$$\frac{1}{2} (\sin^2 \vartheta + \sin^2 \phi)$$

$$= \frac{1}{2}\left(2 - \frac{z^2}{r^2} - \frac{x^2}{r^2}\right)$$

$$= \frac{1}{2}\left(1 + \frac{y^2}{r^2}\right) = \frac{1 + \cos^2 \theta}{2} \tag{6-27}$$

The angle θ is the so-called *scattering angle*, between the direction of the incident beam and OR. Thus, for unpolarized light,

$$\frac{I}{I_0} = \frac{Nk_0^4\alpha^2}{r^2} \frac{1 + \cos^2\theta}{2}$$

$$= \frac{nk_0^4\alpha^2}{r^2} \frac{1 + \cos^2\theta}{2} V$$

where $n\,(= N/V)$ is the number of particles per cubic centimeter and V is the total scattering volume. We may also write

$$\frac{I}{I_0}\frac{r^2}{V} = nk_0^4\alpha^2 \frac{1 + \cos^2\theta}{2} = 16\pi^4 \frac{1 + \cos^2\theta}{2} \frac{n\alpha^2}{\lambda_0^4}$$

and define the Rayleigh ratio R_0 as

$$R_0 = \frac{2}{1 + \cos^2\theta}\frac{I}{I_0}\frac{r^2}{V} = 16\pi^4 \frac{n\alpha^2}{\lambda_0^4}$$

With (6-26) we have

$$\tau = \frac{8\pi}{3} R_0$$

C. Determination of n from Index of Refraction and Turbidity

From measurements of turbidity and index of refraction we really have a method for counting the number of particles per cubic centimeter. Combining (6-2) and (6-26) we get

$$\tau = \frac{32\pi^3}{3} \frac{(\varkappa - 1)^2}{\lambda_0^4} \frac{1}{n}$$

Since $n = N_0\rho/M$, where ρ is the density, M the molecular weight of the particle, and N_0 Avogadro's number,

$$\tau = \frac{32\pi^3}{3} \frac{(\varkappa - 1)^2}{\lambda_0^4} \frac{M}{\rho N_0} = HM\rho \tag{6-28}$$

where the proportionality constant H is a factor characterizing the molecules and may be obtained from refractive-index measurements:

$$H = \frac{32\pi^3}{3} \left(\frac{\varkappa - 1}{\rho}\right)^2 \frac{1}{N_0\lambda_0^4} \tag{6-29}$$

Equation (6-28), already treated by Lord Rayleigh, holds for a gas of low density. For a pure liquid the method followed by Lord Rayleigh carries with it some complications because of interactions between the particles. Einstein (*3*) has shown how these complications can be avoided; he considers the scattering to be caused by local thermal fluctuations in the density of the liquid.

Our next step brings us to solutions. The solvent is made more inhomogeneous when a solute is added. The increase in scattered intensity can be used to count the number of solute particles. If we put

$$\varkappa^2 - \varkappa_0^2 = 4\pi n \alpha \tag{6-30}$$

where $\varkappa$ and $\varkappa_0$ are index of refraction of solution and solvent, respectively, then α is the excess polarizability, which is the polarizability of solution minus that of the solvent. For $\varkappa$ close to $\varkappa_0$, we have $\varkappa^2 - \varkappa_0^2 = (\varkappa + \varkappa_0)(\varkappa - \varkappa_0) \simeq 2\varkappa_0(\varkappa - \varkappa_0)$. Then

$$\varkappa_0(\varkappa - \varkappa_0) = 2\pi n \alpha \tag{6-31}$$

Substituting (6-31) in (6-26) with concentration C instead of density ρ, we get

$$\tau = HMC$$

where

$$H = \frac{32\pi^3}{3} \left(\frac{\varkappa - \varkappa_0}{\varkappa_0 C}\right)^2 \frac{1}{N_0 \lambda^4} \tag{6-32}$$

In Einstein's fluctuation theory, the final result for the turbidity due to fluctuations in concentration (*4, 5*) is

$$\tau = \frac{32\pi^3}{3} \frac{\varkappa_0^2(\varkappa - \varkappa_0)^2}{\lambda_0^4} \frac{1}{C(\partial/\partial C)(P^*/kT)} \tag{6-33}$$

in which P^* is the osmotic pressure. In the limit of high dilution, van't Hoff's relation, $P^* = nkT$, holds in every case; therefore the turbidity of *dilute solutions* due to local fluctuations in concentration can be expressed in the form

$$\tau = \frac{32\pi^3}{3} \frac{\varkappa_0^2(\varkappa - \varkappa_0)^2}{\lambda_0^4} \frac{1}{n} \tag{6-34}$$

or

$$\tau = HMC$$

with

$$H = \frac{32\pi^3}{3} \left(\frac{\varkappa - \varkappa_0}{\varkappa_0} \frac{1}{C} \right)^2 \frac{1}{N_0 \lambda^4} \qquad \lambda = \frac{\lambda_0}{\varkappa_0} \tag{6-35}$$

From measurements of excess turbidity, excess index of refraction, and concentration, the molecular weight of the solute follows at once. The two theories are seen to be equivalent for highly dilute solutions, because (6-32) and (6-35) are the same. For macromolecular solutions the deviations from van't Hoff's law are important, even at high dilutions. In this case we can use (6-33) and write

$$\frac{HC}{\tau} = \frac{\partial}{\partial C} \left(\frac{P^*}{kT} \right) \tag{6-36}$$

in which H is the same fraction constant as defined by (6-32). The osmotic pressure can be expressed in a series expansion:

$$\frac{P^*}{kT} = \frac{C}{M} + BC^2 + \cdots$$

Thus (6-26) has the form

$$H \frac{C}{\tau} = \frac{1}{M} + 2BC + \cdots \tag{6-37}$$

In practice, we can determine H by refraction measurements and τ for a series of concentrations, and then plot HC/τ as a function of C. A straight line drawn through the experimental points cuts the vertical axis of the figure at an ordinate which is equal to $1/M$. The constant B depends on the solvent; B is large and positive with a good solvent. Figure 6-4 shows a plot of HC/τ versus C for polystyrene in toluene and in methyl ethyl ketone (6). Toluene is a better solvent, so the slope of the line for the toluene solution (*a* in Fig. 6-4) is steeper. The straight lines intersect at zero concentration because the molecular weight of the solute is the same. The osmotic pressure decreases but the turbidity increases with increasing molecular weight for a given concentration; therefore, determination of molecular weight by light scattering becomes better when the molecules are bigger.

Light scattering may also be used to study the micelle formation in soap solutions. Figure 6-5 shows typical data in which the turbidity of dodecyl-amine hydrochloride solutions in water are plotted as a function of the concentration of soap (7). There is no measurable turbidity at very low concentrations. Then, the turbidity increases sharply at a certain "critical"

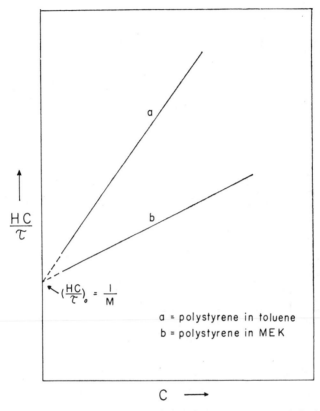

Fig. 6-4. Plot of HC/τ versus C for polystyrene in toluene and in methyl ethyl ketone.

concentration, indicating the formation of micelles. We can determine the size of micelles from these turbidity measurements.

D. Interference and Phase Factor

From (6-19) we have the electric field strength **E** proportional to $e^{i(\omega t - kr)}/r$, where the constant is no longer $k_0 = 2\pi/\lambda_0$, but $k = 2\pi/\lambda$, with $\lambda = \lambda_0/\varkappa_0$. Suppose **S** and $\mathbf{S}_0$ are unit vectors in the direction of primary and secondary rays, as shown in Fig. 6-6. The amplitude, A_s, of the scattered wave from a scattering center located at a distance r from the origin as shown in Fig. 6-7 is proportional to

$$\frac{e^{i\omega t} \exp[-ik(\mathbf{S}_0 \cdot \mathbf{r} + D)]}{D} \tag{6-38}$$

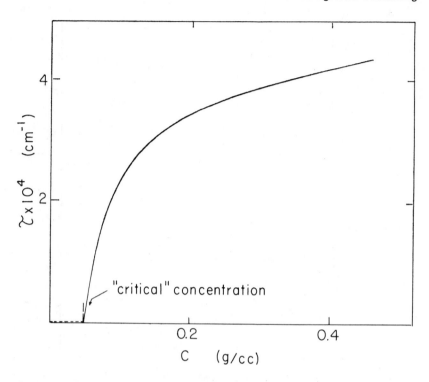

Fig. 6-5. Turbidity of dodecylamine hydrochloride in water as a function of the concentration of soap.

where **r** is the microscopic distance from the origin O to the scattering center, $\mathbf{S}_0 \cdot \mathbf{r}$ gives the phase at the point of scattering due to wave fronts at the origin O, and D is the distance traveled by the scattered wave from the scattering center to the point of observation. Note that a change in

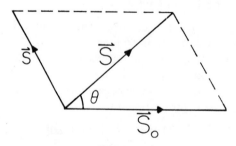

Fig. 6-6.

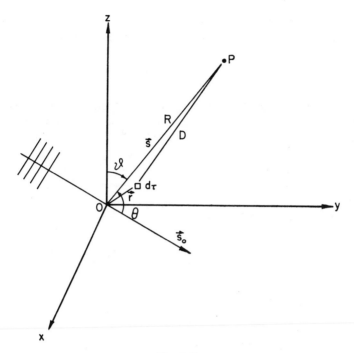

Fig. 6-7.

notation for r has been introduced and $D \gg \mathbf{S_0} \cdot \mathbf{r}$. In addition, because of the microscopic nature of $\mathbf{r}$, D and R are almost parallel. Thus

$$D = R - \mathbf{r} \cdot \mathbf{S} \qquad (6\text{-}39)$$

Substituting (6-39) in (6-38) we get

$$A_s \propto \frac{e^{i\omega t} \exp[-ik(\mathbf{S_0} \cdot \mathbf{r} + R - \mathbf{r} \cdot \mathbf{S})]}{R}$$

If we let $\mathbf{s} = \mathbf{S} - \mathbf{S_0}$, then

$$A_s \propto \frac{e^{-ikR}}{R} e^{i\omega t} e^{i k \mathbf{s} \cdot \mathbf{r}}$$

The factor $(e^{-ikR}/R)e^{i\omega t}$ represents the wave scattered from the origin, and $e^{i k \mathbf{s} \cdot \mathbf{r}}$ is the phase factor which measures the interference between the wavelets emitted by different volume elements. Suppose we can sum the scattering centers of a particle with an integral; then the total amplitude A_t, caused by scattering from various parts of the particle, is

$$A_t \propto \frac{e^{i\omega t}e^{-ikR}}{R} \int_V e^{i\mathbf{ks}\cdot\mathbf{r}} \, d\tau \tag{6-40}$$

where the integration is carried over the volume of the particle. The intensity is the square of the amplitude, or the absolute value of A_t to the square. Let us take a volume element $d\tau$ in this particle and characterize the position of this volume element by drawing a vector $\mathbf{r}$. The scalar product of $\mathbf{s}$ and $\mathbf{r}$ is $sr \cos \beta$, where β is the angle between vectors $\mathbf{s}$ and $\mathbf{r}$. If the particle has different orientations, the observed intensity is the average over all orientations of the particle.

In the case of a sphere with radius a, where $R \gg a$,

$$A_t \propto \int_0^a \int_0^\pi e^{iksr \cos \beta} 2\pi r^2 \sin \beta \, d\beta \, dr$$

$$= \int_0^a 2\pi r^2 \frac{2 \sin ksr}{ksr} \, dr\dagger \tag{6-41}$$

$$= \frac{4\pi}{k^3 s^3} (\sin \alpha - \alpha \cos \alpha) \tag{6-42}$$

with $\alpha = ksa$. If we let the volume of the particle $V = 4\pi a^3/3$, then

$$A_t \propto V\phi(\alpha) \qquad \text{with } \phi(\alpha) = \frac{3}{\alpha^3} (\sin \alpha - \alpha \cos \alpha) \tag{6-43}$$

It may be noted that $\phi(\alpha)$ takes into account the interference from different parts of the molecule and approaches 1 as α approaches 0. The scattered intensity I is proportional to $V^2\phi^2(\alpha)$; this relation affords a method of calculating the size of large particles from measurements of the scattered intensity. $\phi(\alpha) = 0$ when $\alpha = \tan \alpha$, which occurs for $\alpha \simeq 3\pi/2, 5\pi/2, \ldots$, as shown in Fig. 6-8. At the first minimum,

$$ksa = 2ka \sin \frac{\theta}{2} \simeq \frac{3\pi}{2}$$

$\dagger$ Let $\cos \beta = x$, and thus also $-\sin \beta \, d\beta = dx$. Then

$$\int_{-1}^1 e^{iksrx} \, dx = \left. \frac{e^{iksrx}}{iksr} \right|_{1-}^1 = 2 \frac{\sin ksr}{ksr}$$

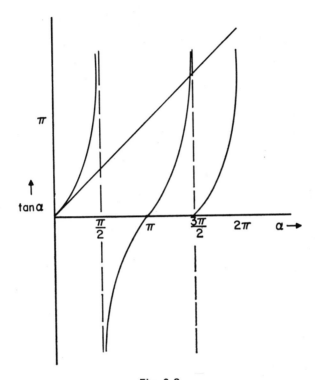

Fig. 6-8.

Suppose we take $\sin(\theta/2) = 1$; then $4\pi a/\lambda \simeq 3\pi/2$ and

$$a \simeq \tfrac{3}{8}\lambda \tag{6-44}$$

Equation (6-44) tells us the condition for the size of the particle, to obtain a minimum in the angular dependence of scattered intensity. Figure 6-9 is a plot of $\phi^2(\alpha)$ versus α.

E. Radius of Gyration

The radius of gyration r_g depends on the distribution of scattering centers as a function of their distance from the center of the particle. By analogy with classical mechanics, it is the second moment of such a distribution of scattering centers. For example, in small-angle X-ray scattering, r_g is the second moment about the electronic center of mass of the particle.

From (6-40) we see that the total amplitude A_t is proportional to

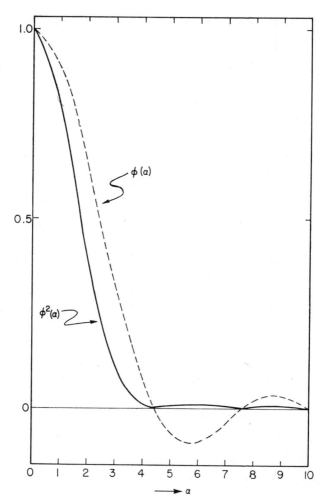

Fig. 6-9. Plot of $\phi^2(\alpha)$ versus α. $\phi(\alpha) = (3/\alpha^3)(\sin \alpha - \alpha \cos \alpha)$.

$\int_V e^{i k s \cdot r}\, d\tau$. A Taylor-series expansion gives $e^{i k s \cdot r} = 1 + i k s \cdot r - \tfrac{1}{2}k^2(s \cdot r)^2 + \cdots$, so that

$$A_t \propto \int_V (1 + i k s \cdot r - \tfrac{1}{2}k^2(s \cdot r)^2 + \cdots)\, d\tau$$

When $s = 0$, $A_0 \propto \int_V d\tau = V =$ scattering volume of the particle.

In rectangular coordinates, $\mathbf{s} \cdot \mathbf{r} = s_x x + s_y y + s_z z$. Then we have

$$A_t \propto V + ik \int_V (s_x x + s_y y + s_z z)\, d\tau - \frac{k^2}{2} \int_V (s_x^2 x^2 + \cdots + 2 s_x s_y xy + \cdots)\, d\tau$$

We may set $\int_V iks_x x\, d\tau = 0$, etc., if we choose the origin of the coordinate system to be at the center of gravity of the particle (which is assumed to be uniform). Thus

$$A_t \propto \int_V \left[1 - \frac{k^2}{2} (\mathbf{s} \cdot \mathbf{r})^2 \right] d\tau$$

$$\propto V \left[1 - \frac{(k^2/2) \int_V (\mathbf{s} \cdot \mathbf{r})^2\, d\tau}{V} \right]$$

Then we find for the instantaneous intensity I_{inst},

$$I_{\text{inst}} \propto V^2 \left[1 - \frac{k^2 \int_V (\mathbf{s} \cdot \mathbf{r})^2\, d\tau}{V} \right]$$

or, using the average for all orientations, we get for the average observed intensity,

$$I \propto V^2 \left[1 - \frac{k^2 \left\langle \int_V (\mathbf{s} \cdot \mathbf{r})^2\, d\tau \right\rangle}{V} \right] \tag{6-45}$$

The notation $\left\langle \int_V (\mathbf{s} \cdot \mathbf{r})^2\, d\tau \right\rangle$ indicates an averaging process in which s is fixed and r rotates in all directions. But rotating r in all directions is the same as holding r fixed (particle fixed) and letting s change in all directions. In other words,

$$\left\langle \int_V (\mathbf{s} \cdot \mathbf{r})^2\, d\tau \right\rangle = \int_V \left\langle (\mathbf{s} \cdot \mathbf{r})^2 \right\rangle d\tau$$

If we express the quantity $(\mathbf{s} \cdot \mathbf{r})^2$ in rectangular coordinates as $(s_x x + s_y y + s_z z)^2$, we shall have three terms of the form $(s_i^2 i^2)$. Let us consider the quantity $\langle s_x^2 x^2 \rangle$. By definition, $s_x = s \cos \gamma$, γ being the angle between s and the x axis (see Fig. 6-10). So

$$\langle s_x^2 x^2 \rangle = x^2 \int_0^\pi \frac{s^2 \cos^2 \gamma\, 2\pi \sin \gamma\, d\gamma}{4\pi} = \frac{s^2 x^2}{3}$$

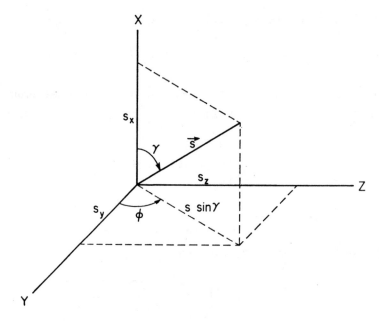

Fig. 6-10.

There will be similar terms in y and z. The cross terms vanish; for example,

$$\langle s_x s_y xy \rangle \propto \frac{1}{4\pi} \int_{\phi=0}^{2\pi} \int_{\gamma=0}^{\pi} s \cos \gamma \, s \sin \gamma \cos \phi \sin \gamma \, d\gamma \, d\phi = 0$$

Then

$$\int_V \langle (\mathbf{s} \cdot \mathbf{r})^2 \rangle \, d\tau = \frac{s^2}{3} \int_V (x^2 + y^2 + z^2) \, d\tau = \frac{s^2}{3} \int_V r^2 \, d\tau$$

Finally, (6-45) has the form

$$I \propto V^2 \left(1 - \frac{k^2 s^2}{3} \frac{\int_V r^2 \, d\tau}{V} \right)$$

Since the radius of gyration r_g is defined according to the relation

$$r_g^2 = \frac{\int_V r^2 \, d\tau}{V}$$

we can write

$$I \propto V^2 \left(1 - \frac{k^2 s^2 r_g^2}{3} \right) \tag{6-46}$$

If we plot the scattered intensity versus s^2 [$= 4 \sin^2(\theta/2)$], the curve starts with a finite tangent. We only have to know this tangent to compute the size of the particle, provided every internal volume element of the particle scatters in the same way. So, in the first approximation, we can calculate particle size in terms of the radius of gyration from the scattered intensity as a function of the scattering angle. It should be emphasized that we can experimentally obtain the radius of gyration for macromolecules regardless of their forms.

6-2. SCATTERING BY MEDIUM WITH IRREGULAR VARIATION OF DIELECTRIC CONSTANT

There is interference in a medium in which the particles are very near each other, or in any liquid system for which thermal density or concentration fluctuations are present.

Let us assume a medium with an average dielectric constant ϵ_0 on top of which local fluctuations $\eta(x, y, z)$ of random character are superimposed. Through this medium we send a plane-polarized primary light in which the electric-field vector has an amplitude E_0.

The Maxwell equations [from (6-16)] for a medium with a dielectric constant that fluctuates have the form

$$ik_0 \mathbf{H} = - \text{curl } \mathbf{E} \qquad ik_0(\epsilon_0 + \eta)\mathbf{E} = \text{curl } \mathbf{H}$$
$$\text{div } \mathbf{H} = 0 \qquad \text{div}[(\epsilon_0 + \eta)\mathbf{E}] = 0 \tag{6-47}$$

We put a corresponding perturbation in the electric and magnetic field intensity, so that

$$\mathbf{E} = \mathbf{E}_0 + \mathbf{E}_1 \qquad \mathbf{H} = \mathbf{H}_0 + \mathbf{H}_1 \tag{6-48}$$

The time dependence of the field is being neglected because of the cisoidal nature of the solutions, which means that separation of space and time is always possible. Substituting (6-48) in (6-47) we get for the first-order perturbation,

$$ik_0 \mathbf{H}_1 = - \text{curl } \mathbf{E}_1 \qquad ik_0 \epsilon_0 \mathbf{E}_1 + ik_0 \eta \mathbf{E}_0 = \text{curl } \mathbf{H}_1$$
$$\text{div } \mathbf{H}_1 = 0 \qquad \epsilon_0 \text{ div } \mathbf{E}_1 + \text{div}(\eta \mathbf{E}_0) = 0 \tag{6-49}$$

Higher-order terms are being neglected. Let

$$H_1 = \text{curl } A_1 \tag{6-50}$$

Remembering $\partial/\partial t \equiv i\omega$, we get, from (6-12),

$$E_1 = -ik_0 A_1 - \text{grad } \phi \tag{6-51}$$

Substituting (6-50), (6-51), (6-14), and (6-14a) in the equation $ik_0\epsilon_0 E_1 + ik_0\eta E_0 = \text{curl } H_1$ [from (6-49)] we obtain

$$ik_0\epsilon_0(-ik_0 A_1 - \text{grad } \phi) + ik_0\eta E_0 = \text{curl curl } A_1 = \text{grad div } A_1 - \nabla^2 A_1 \tag{6-52}$$

From (6-51) and the relation $\epsilon_0 \text{ div } E_1 + \text{div}(\eta E_0) = 0$, we have

$$-ik_0\epsilon_0 \text{ div } A_1 - \epsilon_0\nabla^2\phi + \text{div}(\eta E_0) = 0$$

If we take [from (6-13)] $\text{div } A_1 \simeq -ik_0\epsilon_0\phi$, and neglect the higher-order terms, the final result from (6-52) is

$$\nabla^2 A_1 + \epsilon_0 k_0^2 A_1 = -ik_0\eta E_0 \tag{6-53}$$

Thus it follows from Maxwell's equations that by putting $E = E_0 + E_1$ and $H = H_0 + H_1$, a vector potential A can again be defined such that

$$\nabla^2 A + \varkappa_0^2 k_0^2 A = -ik_0\eta E_0 \tag{6-53a}$$

holds instead of (6-14a). Accordingly, we can calculate A:

$$A = \frac{ik_0 E_0}{4\pi} \int \eta \frac{e^{-ikr}}{r} d\tau$$

From (6-18) we know that if we have an induced dipole of moment μ, the corresponding vector potential is $A = ik_0\mu(e^{-ikr}/r)k$. So we see that each space element acts like a dipole and the moment is

$$\mu = \frac{\eta E_0}{4\pi} d\tau$$

Thus, from (6-19) and (6-40) we find that the electric field E created by a volume V in which the fluctuations of the dielectric constant η will be, at a large distance R from this volume (acting as the center of scattered radiations) (8),

$$E = \int_V \frac{\eta E_0}{4\pi} k_0^2 e^{ik(s \cdot r)} d\tau \sin \vartheta \frac{e^{i(\omega t - kR)}}{R} \tag{6-54}$$

Neglecting the time dependence, we find

$$E = E_0 \frac{e^{-ikR}}{R} \frac{k^2}{4\pi} \sin \vartheta \int_V \frac{\eta}{\epsilon_0} e^{ik(\mathbf{s} \cdot \mathbf{r})} \, d\tau \qquad (6\text{-}55)$$

In this relation, $k = 2\pi/\lambda$, λ being the wavelength in the medium. The angle between the directions of E_0 and R is called ϑ; the vector $\mathbf{s} = \mathbf{S} - \mathbf{S}_0$, where $\mathbf{S}$ is a unit vector in the direction of R and $\mathbf{S}_0$ is a unit vector in the direction of propagation of the primary wave. If θ is the angle between $\mathbf{S}$ and $\mathbf{S}_0$, $s = 2 \sin(\theta/2)$. The vector $\mathbf{r}$ defines the position of the volume element $d\tau$ in the scattering volume with respect to an arbitrary center; from it the large distance R is measured. The quantity $e^{ik\mathbf{s} \cdot \mathbf{r}}$ is the phase factor and V is the scattering volume.

From relation (6-55) the instantaneous scattered intensity I_{inst} is calculated to be

$$I_{\text{inst}} = EE^* = \frac{k^4 E_0^2}{16\pi^2} \frac{\sin^2 \vartheta}{R^2} \iint \left(\frac{\eta}{\epsilon_0}\right) \left(\frac{\eta}{\epsilon_0}\right)' e^{ik(\mathbf{s} \cdot (\mathbf{r} - \mathbf{r}'))} \, d\tau \, d\tau' \qquad (6\text{-}56)$$

where E^* is the complex conjugate of E. The fluctuation η varies with time, but in the laboratory usually only the time average of the scattered intensity I is being measured. Furthermore, we can replace the time average by a space average, because the position of the sample has no influence on the observed intensity if the fluctuations are "frozen in." Thus

$$\frac{I}{I_0} = \frac{k^4}{16\pi^2} \frac{\sin^2 \vartheta}{R^2} \iint \left\langle \left(\frac{\eta}{\epsilon_0}\right)_A \left(\frac{\eta}{\epsilon_0}\right)_B \right\rangle e^{ik(\mathbf{s} \cdot (\mathbf{r}_A - \mathbf{r}_B))} \, d\tau_A \, d\tau_B \qquad (6\text{-}57)$$

The quantity $(\eta/\epsilon_0)_i$ represents the fluctuation measured at point i and the symbol $\langle \rangle$ indicates an average value. In an isotropic medium the product of two fluctuations is a function only of the distance AB, which is $AB = \mathbf{r} = \mathbf{r}_A - \mathbf{r}_B$. In the case of stationary fluctuations, the average value of the product is obtained by letting the "measuring stick" AB take up all possible positions and orientations within the scattering volume.

A. Correlation Function

We now introduce a correlation function $C(r)$ by the definition

$$\left\langle \left(\frac{\eta}{\epsilon_0}\right)_A \left(\frac{\eta}{\epsilon_0}\right)_B \right\rangle = C(r) \left\langle \left(\frac{\eta}{\epsilon_0}\right)_2 \right\rangle \qquad (6\text{-}58)$$

The correlation function is dimensionless; $C(r) = 1$ for $r = 0$, and $C(r)$ tends to zero for large values of r. The correlation function $C(r)$ may be interpreted as follows: Let us first pass a line through the interior of a liquid and plot the index of refraction with all its fluctuations perpendicular to this line, as shown schematically in Fig. 6-11. This is an instantaneous

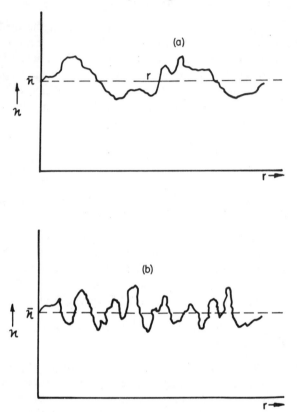

Fig. 6-11. (a) Instantaneous index of refraction as a function of position (long "correlation" length). (b) Instantaneous index of refraction as a function of position (short "correlation" length).

picture, because the local index of refraction is going to change from moment to moment. The dashed line in Fig. 6-11 indicates an average index of refraction, which is what we measure when we use a refractometer. For example, benzene would have a refractive index of 1.50142 at 20°C with an incident wavelength of 5890 A. The intensity of light which is scattered will depend on the average square of the amplitude of these fluctuations. But we should also note that changing from a positive to a negative fluctuation takes a certain distance, which can be quite different in different cases, such as Fig. 6-11(a) and (b), illustrating cases with the same amplitude but a different variation of the fluctuation. A fast variation in the index of refraction would indicate a shorter "wavelength"; the correlation function is a way of characterizing this "wavelength."

To measure the correlation function we imagine that we throw a stick AB (with a length r) into the liquid and measure the fluctuations at both ends. Then we make a product Δ_A by Δ_B, where Δ_i represents local fluctuations at i. After throwing the stick many times at random into the liquid, we can get the average value of the product, $\langle\Delta_A\Delta_B\rangle$. The average value for a stick with no length represents the average square of the fluctuations $\langle\Delta^2\rangle$. As the stick gets longer, the product $\langle\Delta_A\Delta_B\rangle$ gets smaller, because if the stick is very long, what happens at one end is almost completely independent of what happens at the other end; so $C(r)$ approaches zero as r approaches infinity. Plotting the fluctuations in our two cases [Fig. 6-11(a) and (b)], we shall get $C(r)$ starting at 1 for zero distance and falling off faster for the material with smaller fluctuations, as shown in Fig. 6-12.

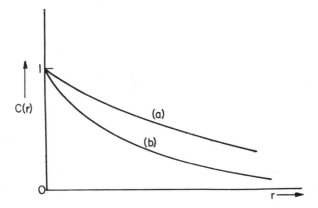

Fig. 6-12. Schematic representation of the correlation function for random structures (no maxima or minima); curve (a) represents Fig. 6-11(a) and curve (b) represents Fig. 6-11(b).

Maxima and minima in the correlation curve are absent for noncrystalline media where random structure persists. Thus the correlation function can fall off very fast or it can go down slowly—and a certain characteristic length is involved. We can, for instance, ask: "How long a stick do we have to make to get $C(r)$ from the value 1 to the value $\frac{1}{2}$?" This is in essence what we would call the persistence length L, the length over which a certain fluctuation persists before it changes to the other direction. The analytical expression for the persistence length will be given shortly.

Substituting (6-58) in (6-57) we find

$$\frac{I}{I_0} = \frac{k^4}{16\pi^2} \frac{\sin^2 \vartheta}{R^2} \left\langle \left(\frac{\eta}{\epsilon_0}\right)^2 \right\rangle V \int C(r) e^{ik(\mathbf{s} \cdot \mathbf{r})} \, d\tau \tag{6-59}$$

in which V is the scattering volume. The interference effect appears as a result of the correlation of the fluctuations in neighboring points. From (6-41) we know that the presence of spherical symmetry reduces

$$\int C(r) e^{ik(\mathbf{s} \cdot \mathbf{r})} \, d\tau = \int_0^\infty \int_0^\pi C(r) e^{iksr \cos \beta} 2\pi r^2 \sin \beta \, d\beta \, dr$$

to

$$4\pi \int_0^\infty C(r) \frac{\sin ksr}{ksr} r^2 \, dr$$

This leads to the final result

$$\frac{I}{I_0} = \frac{\sin^2 \vartheta}{R^2} \frac{k^4}{16\pi^2} \left\langle \left(\frac{\eta}{\epsilon_0}\right)^2 \right\rangle V \int C(r) \frac{\sin ksr}{ksr} \, d\tau \tag{6-60}$$

For small values of s,

$$\frac{I}{I_0} = \frac{\sin^2 \vartheta}{R^2} \frac{k^4}{16\pi^2} \left\langle \left(\frac{\eta}{\epsilon_0}\right)^2 \right\rangle V \left[\int C(r) \, d\tau - \frac{k^2 s^2}{6} \int r^2 C(r) d\tau + \cdots \right]$$

If we take

$$I_{max} = I_0 \frac{\sin^2 \vartheta}{R^2} \frac{k^4}{16\pi^2} \left\langle \left(\frac{\eta}{\epsilon_0}\right)^2 \right\rangle V \int C(r) \, d\tau$$

which is the scattered intensity for $s = 0$, and define a persistence length L such that

$$L^2 = \frac{\int r^2 C(r) \, d\tau}{\int C(r) \, d\tau}$$

then

$$\frac{I}{I_{max}} = 1 - \frac{k^2 s^2 L^2}{6} + \cdots \tag{6-60a}$$

Therefore, when the persistence length is zero, the scattered intensity is independent of the scattering angle. When the persistence length becomes larger, the scattered intensity varies with the angle of observation, and L^2 can be calculated from measurements of the angular dependence of scattered intensity.

It may be noted from (6-60a) that the term $k^2s^2L^2/6$ becomes increasingly important when it reaches the order of 1. If the persistence length L is small, we can design our experiments so that the term $k^2s^2L^2/6$ still approaches 1. Since $k = 2\pi/\lambda$ and $s = 2\sin(\theta/2)$, a decrease in the wavelength λ or an increase in the scattering angle θ could enhance the effect we want to observe. For example, suppose $L = 1000$ A; then we could measure the scattered intensity either in the visible range (say $\lambda = 3000$ A), with "normal" angles of observation (say for θ between 25 and 145°), or in the X-ray range (say $\lambda = 1.54$ A), with very small angles of observation. In the case of small-angle X-ray scattering, if we start our measurements from the lowest measurable angle where the background scattering remains tolerable, the scattering curves can experimentally be connected for both light and X-ray radiation from a plot of the scattered intensity versus s/λ.

If the primary radiation is unpolarized, it is only necessary to replace $\sin^2 \vartheta$ by $(1 + \cos^2 \theta)/2$ [see the derivation of (6-27)].

B. Calculation of Correlation Function from Intensity Distribution

For a noncrystalline medium the correlation function plays the same role as does the lattice structure and the distribution of the atoms within the lattice cell play for a crystalline medium. It is important to see how the correlation function can be derived from observations of the angular distribution of scattered intensity. In principle, the solution to this problem can be obtained by the application of a Fourier inversion.

We know that if

$$F(x) = 2 \int_0^\infty f(y)\sin 2\pi xy \, dy$$

then the corresponding $f(y)$ is

$$f(y) = 2 \int_0^\infty F(x)\sin 2\pi xy \, dx$$

From our measurements of scattered intensities I at various angles θ, we can obtain from (6-60) a plot of $\Omega(ks)$ versus s/λ, where Ω is defined as

$$\Omega(ks) = \int_0^\infty C(r) \frac{\sin ksr}{ksr} \, d\tau \tag{6-61}$$

The function $\Omega(ks)$ describes the angular-intensity distribution. In terms of s/λ, (6-61) can also have the form

$$\frac{s}{\lambda}\Omega\left(\frac{s}{\lambda}\right) = 2\int_0^\infty rC(r)\sin\left(2\pi\frac{s}{\lambda}r\right) dr \tag{6-61a}$$

Suppose $F(x) \equiv (s/\lambda)\Omega(s/\lambda)$, $x \equiv s/\lambda$, $f(y) \equiv rC(r)$, and $y \equiv r$; then by application of the Fourier theorem, we have

$$rC(r) = 2\int_0^\infty \frac{s}{\lambda}\Omega\left(\frac{s}{\lambda}\right)\sin\left(2\pi r\frac{s}{\lambda}\right) d\left(\frac{s}{\lambda}\right) \tag{6-62}$$

In actual practice, the curve for $\Omega(s/\lambda)$ is known only for a finite interval, instead of for the required range from 0 to ∞, because the range of $s [= 2\sin(\theta/2)]$ is limited from 0 to 2. We can try to stretch the magnitude of s/λ by using decreasing wavelength, as in the combined technique of light scattering and small-angle X-ray scattering.

If the correlation function is a simple exponential,

$$C(r) = e^{-r/a}$$

the corresponding expression for $\Omega(s/\lambda)$ is represented by a simple formula. The integration by which the volume Ω is defined can be performed readily and leads to

$$\Omega\left(\frac{s}{\lambda}\right) = \frac{8\pi a^3}{(1 + k^2s^2a^2)^2} \tag{6-63}$$

Since the scattered intensity is proportional to $\Omega(s/\lambda)$, the corresponding intensity distribution can be checked by plotting the reciprocal of the square root of the scattered intensity as a function of s^2. If the correlation function is indeed a simple exponential, this procedure gives a straight line, the slope of which is a measure of the correlation length a.

With reference to our general formula for the scattered intensity, (6-63) shows that, for large-enough values of s, the intensity decreases in proportion to s^{-4}. This feature turns out to be quite general, independent of the special form of the correlation function.

Another approach to an expression for $\Omega(s/\lambda)$, when the form of $C(r)$ is not known, is to develop (6-61), using the substitution of a variable $\sigma (= ks)$:

$$\Omega = -4\pi\frac{1}{\sigma}\frac{d}{d\sigma}\int_0^\infty C(r)\cos\sigma r\, dr \tag{6-64}$$

The integral can be developed in powers of $1/\sigma$ by repeated partial integration:

$$\int_0^\infty C(r) \cos \sigma r \; dr = \frac{C'(0)}{\sigma^2} + \cdots$$

which makes

$$\Omega = -8\pi \frac{C'(0)}{\sigma^4} + \cdots = -\frac{8\pi}{k^4} \frac{C'(0)}{s^4} + \cdots \tag{6-65}$$

Equation (6-65) is valid provided $C(r)$ vanishes rapidly enough for large values of r and provided a finite gradient of $C(r)$ for $r = 0$ exists.

6-3. CRITICAL OPALESCENCE OF ONE-COMPONENT SYSTEMS

The light scattering by gases and liquids under ordinary conditions is weak and obeys Rayleigh's law, which shows no angular dissymmetry; i.e., for plane-polarized light, where the electric vector is perpendicular to the plane of scattering, the scattered intensity is the same at all angles. However, in the vicinity of the critical point, whether it is a one-component or a two-component system, very strong scattering of visible light is observed and the medium looks turbid. This is the so-called *critical opalescence*. At the same time, the scattered intensity becomes concentrated more and more in the forward direction (the direction of propagation of the primary beam) as the critical temperature is approached (*9–14*).

Equations (6-60) and (6-61) tell us that the angular dissymmetry indicates the existence of an appreciable correlation of the local density or local concentration fluctuations over distances comparable to the wavelength of visible light.

In 1917 Zernike (*15, 16*) and Ornstein and Zernike (*17, 18*) pointed out that it is necessary to consider two effects to explain the phenomenon of critical opalescence: the amplitude of the fluctuation and the length over which the fluctuation extends. In 1933 Rocard (*19*) again stressed the effect of the gradient of fluctuation on scattered intensity near the critical point. The second effect was not taken into account in Einstein's fluctuation theory. Einstein assumed that the thermal motions of neighboring molecules were independent of one another. Consequently, his theory predicts a scattered intensity independent of the angle of observation, even in the neighborhood of the critical point. The scattering theory must be modified so that it takes care of the dissymmetry effect near the critical point but can be reduced to Einstein's theory when measurements are made far from the critical point.

Let us begin our consideration of critical opalescence by developing the basic Einstein equation. Following Einstein, we accept the thermal molecular motion as the reason for fluctuations. However, it will be more appropriate in our actual derivation to use a line of reasoning followed by Brillouin (*20*). Connection between density fluctuations and the scattered intensity observable at a definite angle is made by means of a Fourier analysis of the local fluctuations. The Fourier analysis represents, in its physical interpretation, a description of the thermal motion of molecules in the liquid as a superposition of supersonic waves with varying directions and varying wavelengths. Brillouin starts out by calculating the scattered intensity of a homogeneous liquid through which a sonic wave travels. The sonic wave induces small periodic fluctuations η of the dielectric constant ϵ_0. Experiments on the scattering of light by artificial supersonic waves were performed by Debye and Sears (*21*). If a wave passes through the liquid in a direction indicated by the unit vector $\mathbf{S}$, the periodic fluctuations η in the dielectric constant at a point $\mathbf{r}$ can be represented by

$$\eta = \eta_0 \cos(\Omega t - K(\mathbf{S} \cdot \mathbf{r}) \; \dagger \tag{6-66}$$

in which K is $2\pi/\Lambda$ and Λ is the wavelength of the supersonic wave. Note that $\mathbf{S}$ is a unit vector representing the direction of propagation of the supersonic wave, *not* that of the scattered light. We know from relation (6-55) that the electric field E created by a volume V in which the fluctuations of the dielectric constant are η will be, at a large distance R from this volume (acting as the center of scattered radiation),

$$E = E_0 \frac{e^{-ikR}}{R} \frac{k^2}{4\pi} \sin \vartheta \int_V \frac{\eta}{\epsilon_0} e^{ik(\mathbf{s} \cdot \mathbf{r})} \, d\tau \tag{6-55}$$

where $k = 2\pi/\lambda$, λ being the wavelength of light in the medium. The reader may refer to the original equation for details of the symbols. The time dependence of E, a factor $e^{i\omega t}$, has been neglected.

Substituting relation (6-66) in (6-55) and introducing the time dependence, we get

$$E = E_0 \frac{e^{-ikR}}{R} \frac{k^2}{4\pi} \sin \vartheta \int_V \frac{\eta_0}{\epsilon_0} e^{i\omega t} e^{ik(\mathbf{s} \cdot \mathbf{r})} \cos(\Omega t - K(\mathbf{S} \cdot \mathbf{r})) \, d\tau$$

† In general, such periodic fluctuations may also be represented by

$$\eta = \eta_0 \exp\{i[\Omega t - K(\mathbf{S} \cdot \mathbf{r})]\}$$

However, only the real part has physical significance here.

or

$$E = E_0 \frac{e^{-ikR}}{R} \frac{k^2}{4\pi} \sin \vartheta \frac{\eta_0}{\epsilon_0} X$$

where

$$X = \int_V e^{i\omega t} e^{ik(\mathbf{s} \cdot \mathbf{r})} \cos(\Omega t - K(\mathbf{S} \cdot \mathbf{r})) \, d\tau \qquad (6\text{-}67)$$

The integral X expresses the time dependence of, and interference between, the wavelets emitted by different volume elements and induced by one possible variation of the supersonic waves traveling through a liquid. Since

$$\cos x = \frac{e^{ix} + e^{-ix}}{2}$$

X may be separated into two terms,

$$X = X_1 + X_2$$

$$X = \frac{1}{2} \int_V e^{i(\omega + \Omega)t} e^{i[(ks - KS) \cdot \mathbf{r}]} \, d\tau + \frac{1}{2} \int_V e^{i(\omega - \Omega)t} e^{i[(ks + KS) \cdot \mathbf{r}]} \, d\tau \qquad (6\text{-}68)$$

In performing the integration of X_1, we let $KS - ks = \mathbf{P}$. The vector $\mathbf{P}$ has to cover K space with the end of vector ks as centrum. Thus

$$X_1 = \frac{1}{2} \int e^{-i(\mathbf{P} \cdot \mathbf{r})} \, d\tau e^{i(\omega + \Omega)t}$$

which resembles (6-40). Using (6-42) and (6-43), we obtain for the spherically symmetric case,

$$X_1 = \frac{1}{2} V \phi(x) e^{i(\omega + \Omega)t} \qquad (6\text{-}69)$$

with $\phi(x) = (3/x^3)(\sin x - x \cos x)$ and $x = Pa$, or

$$X_1^2 = \frac{1}{4} V^2 \phi^2(x) \cos^2(\Omega + \omega)t \qquad (6\text{-}70)$$

So far we have taken into consideration the effect of one possible vibration; X_1^2 must now be summed over all possible vibrations. For this calculation we need the number of free vibrations in a volume V, which may be calculated as follows.

Consider a region of space, defined by $0 < x < a$, $0 < y < a$, $0 < z < a$, enclosed in a cubic box with perfectly reflecting walls for sound waves, or perfectly conducting walls, in the case of electromagnetic waves. The

boundary condition for standing waves between the walls of the box is
that the waves must have nodes at the surface of the walls. Thus we have

$$a = l\frac{\Lambda}{2}\frac{1}{\cos \alpha_l}$$

$$a = m\frac{\Lambda}{2}\frac{1}{\cos \alpha_m}$$

$$a = n\frac{\Lambda}{2}\frac{1}{\cos \alpha_n}$$

where l, m, and n are the number of segments into which the edges of the
cube are divided; Λ is the wavelength of supersonic waves; and $\cos \alpha_l$,
$\cos \alpha_m$, and $\cos \alpha_n$ are the direction cosines of the normal to the plane
wave. Since

$$\cos^2 \alpha_l + \cos^2 \alpha_m + \cos^2 \alpha_n = 1$$

we get for our boundary condition,

$$\frac{4a^2}{\Lambda^2} = l^2 + m^2 + n^2$$

or

$$\frac{K^2 a^2}{\pi^2} = l^2 + m^2 + n^2 \qquad (6\text{-}71)$$

in which $K = 2\pi/\Lambda$. Equation (6-71) expresses the number of possible
vibrations of wavelength Λ in terms of the number of groups of their
integers, l, m, and n. The number of groups of three *positive* integers, Z,
represents the number of free vibrations in the box, and is one-eighth the
number of vibrations in a sphere with radius $R = Ka/\pi$. Thus

$$Z = \frac{1}{8}\frac{4\pi}{3}\left(\frac{Ka}{\pi}\right)^3 = \frac{a^3}{6\pi^2} K^3$$

The propagation vector $K = 2\pi/\Lambda = \Omega/C$, in which Ω and C are the
angular frequency and the velocity of propagation of the supersonic wave.
Thus, since $\Omega = 2\pi N$, with N representing the supersonic frequency,

$$Z = \frac{4\pi}{3}\frac{N^3}{C^3} a^3$$

and

$$dZ = \frac{V_s}{C^3} N^2 \, dN \, dW \qquad \text{or} \qquad dZ = \frac{V_s}{(2\pi)^3} K^2 \, dK \, dW$$

where dW is an element of the solid angle. Here dZ is the number of independent waves in a volume V_s in the interval dW and is equivalent to the density of points (each representing a possible vibration) in K space:

$$dZ = \frac{V_s}{(2\pi)^3} K^2 \, dK \, dW = \frac{V_s}{(2\pi)^3} P^2 \, dP \, dW \tag{6-72}$$

Thus

$$\sum X_1^2 = \tfrac{1}{4} V^2 \cos^2(\Omega + \omega) t \frac{V_s}{(2\pi)^3} \int \phi^2(x) P^2 \, dP \, dW$$

$$= \tfrac{1}{4} V^2 \cos^2(\Omega + \omega) t \frac{(4\pi/3) a^3}{(2\pi)^3} \int_0^\infty \frac{9}{x^6} (\sin x - x \cos x)^2 \frac{x^2 \, dx}{a^3} 4\pi$$

$$= \tfrac{1}{4} V^2 \cos^2(\Omega + \omega) t \frac{6}{\pi} \int_0^\infty \frac{(\sin x - x \cos x)^2}{x^4} \, dx \; \dagger$$

From this we make the evaluation

$$\sum X_1^2 = \tfrac{1}{4} V^2 \cos^2(\Omega + \omega) t \tag{6-73}$$

In X_1 the only part of the integration interval which is important is the part that satisfies the condition

$$ks - KS = 0 \tag{6-74}$$

This conclusion comes from the results of the calculation for all possible variations of independent sonic waves, as we have shown in (6-73). Thus, of all the supersonic waves which are traversing the liquid, only one is effective for the scattering. It is a wave with a front such that the scattered light can be considered as primary light reflected at this front. s and S have

† The integral can be evaluated as follows:

$$\int_0^\infty \frac{(\sin x - x \cos x)^2}{x^4} \, dx = \left[(\sin x - x \cos x)^2 \frac{x^{-3}}{-3} \right]_0^\infty + \frac{2}{3} \int_0^\infty \sin x (\sin x - x \cos x) \frac{dx}{x^2}$$

$$\int_0^\infty \sin x \cos x \frac{dx}{x} = \frac{1}{2} \int_0^\infty \sin 2x \frac{dx}{x} = \frac{1}{2} \int_0^\infty \sin u \frac{du}{u}$$

$$\int_0^\infty \sin^2 x \frac{dx}{x^2} = \left[\sin^2 x \frac{x^{-1}}{-1} \right]_0^\infty + \int_0^\infty \frac{dx}{x} 2 \sin x \cos x = \int_0^\infty \sin u \frac{du}{u}$$

Therefore,

$$\int_0^\infty (\sin x - x \cos x)^2 \frac{dx}{x^4} = \left(\frac{2}{3} - \frac{1}{3} \right) \int_0^\infty \sin u \frac{du}{u} = \frac{\pi}{6}$$

the same direction, and (6-74), in fact, represents Bragg's law (as shown in Fig. 6-13),

$$\frac{s}{\lambda} = \frac{1}{\Lambda} \qquad (6\text{-}75)$$

which relates the wavelength λ of the light to the wavelength Λ of the reflecting sonic wave. It may be noted in (6-70) that the scattered light also

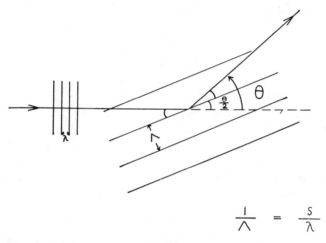

$$\frac{1}{\Lambda} = \frac{s}{\lambda}$$

Fig. 6-13. Brillouin scattering of light waves λ by supersonic wave fronts of wavelength Λ.

has different frequencies, indicating a Doppler effect (*21–24*). Combining results from (6-55), (6-68), and (6-73) we find

$$E^2 = E_0^2 \frac{k^4}{16\pi^2} \frac{\sin^2 \vartheta}{R^2} \left(\frac{\eta_0}{\epsilon_0}\right)^2 V^2 \left(\frac{1}{4} + \frac{1}{4}\right) \qquad (6\text{-}76)$$

with the two integrals in X [Eq. (6-68)] corresponding to two reflecting sonic waves, the one giving a frequency $\Omega + \omega$ and the other $\Omega - \omega$.

If $\rho = \rho_0 + \sigma$, ρ being the density of the liquid, ρ_0 the average density of the liquid, and σ_0 the amplitude of the density fluctuations, we can express η_0 in terms of σ_0 by the relation

$$\frac{\eta_0}{\epsilon_0} = \frac{\sigma_0}{\rho_0} \frac{\rho}{\epsilon} \frac{d\epsilon}{d\rho}$$

provided every density fluctuation means a fluctuation in the dielectric constant. The energy of a wave of amplitude σ_0 going through a volume V corresponds to

$$\frac{V}{2\kappa}\left(\frac{\sigma_0}{\rho_0}\right)^2$$

where κ is the compressibility. This energy should be equal to βT in thermal equilibrium (β is Boltzmann's constant). So we have

$$V\left(\frac{\sigma_0}{\rho_0}\right)^2 = 2\kappa\beta T$$

and finally

$$\frac{I}{I_0} = \frac{k^4}{16\pi^2}\frac{\sin^2\vartheta}{R^2}\left(\frac{\rho\,d\epsilon}{\epsilon\,d\rho}\right)^2 V\kappa\beta T \qquad (6\text{-}77)$$

This is the result first derived by Einstein (3). In this relation the scattered intensity is independent of the angle of observation if we use polarized light whose electric vector is perpendicular to the plane of observation.

We shall use relation (6-77) to calculate the turbidities of water and benzene as two illustrations. The experimental data are:

	Water	Benzene
Index of refraction ($\varkappa$)	1.33	1.50
Compressibility ($cm^2/dyne$)	45×10^{-12}	90×10^{-12}

If we assume the Lorentz-Lorenz expression holds for liquids such as water and benzene, then

$$\frac{\epsilon - 1}{\epsilon + 2} = \frac{4\pi}{3}n\alpha$$

in which ϵ is the dielectric constant of the liquid, n the number of molecules per cubic centimeter, and α the polarizability. With variation in n we get

$$\frac{(\epsilon + 2) - (\epsilon - 1)}{(\epsilon + 2)^2}\frac{d\epsilon}{dn} = \frac{4\pi}{3}\alpha$$

or

$$\frac{3}{(\epsilon + 2)^2}n\frac{d\epsilon}{dn} = \frac{4\pi}{3}n\alpha = \frac{\epsilon - 1}{\epsilon + 2}$$

Therefore,

$$\frac{\rho\,d\epsilon}{\epsilon\,d\rho} = \frac{n}{\epsilon}\frac{d\epsilon}{dn} = \frac{1}{\epsilon}\frac{\epsilon - 1}{\epsilon + 2}\frac{(\epsilon + 2)^2}{3} = \frac{(\epsilon - 1)(\epsilon + 2)}{3\epsilon}$$

With Maxwell's relation $\epsilon = \varkappa^2$ we can write

$$\frac{\rho}{\epsilon} \frac{d\epsilon}{d\rho} = \frac{(\varkappa^2 - 1)(\varkappa^2 + 2)}{3\varkappa^2}$$

The total energy loss per second can be calculated by integrating (6-77) over all scattering angles. For unpolarized light, we get

$$\text{total energy loss per second} = 2\pi V \int_0^\pi I_0 \frac{A}{R^2} R^2 \sin\theta \, d\theta \frac{1 + \cos^2\theta}{2}$$

with

$$A = \frac{k^4}{16\pi^2} \left(\frac{\rho}{\epsilon} \frac{d\epsilon}{d\rho}\right)^2 \kappa\beta T$$

Letting $y = \cos\theta$, we then get

$$\text{total energy loss per second} = I_0 2\pi A V \int_0^1 (1 + y^2) \, dy = \frac{8\pi}{3} A V I_0$$

If I_0 is the energy carried through 1 cm²/sec, then such a beam, going through our solution, will lose intensity in the direction of propagation according to the relation

$$-\frac{dI}{dx} = \left(\frac{8\pi}{3} A\right) I_0 = \tau I_0$$

The quantity in parentheses is what is generally called the *turbidity* (6-25), which we indicate by τ. We therefore come to the conclusion that

$$\tau = \frac{8\pi}{3} A$$

$$= \frac{k^4}{6\pi} \left(\frac{\rho}{\epsilon} \frac{d\epsilon}{d\rho}\right)^2 \kappa\beta T$$

$$= \frac{8\pi^3}{3} \left(\frac{\rho}{\epsilon} \frac{d\epsilon}{d\rho}\right)^2 \frac{\kappa\beta T}{\lambda^4}$$

$$= \frac{8\pi^3}{3} \frac{(\varkappa^2 - 1)(\varkappa^2 + 2)}{3\varkappa^2} \frac{\kappa\beta T}{\lambda^4}$$

With $\lambda_0 = 4000$ A, water and benzene have 1.01×10^{-4} and 4.52×10^{-4} cm^{-1}, respectively, as their calculated turbidities.

A. Free Energy of a van der Waals Gas with Variable Density (25)

For a van der Waals gas in an isothermal reversible process, the molar Helmholtz free energy for a homogeneous liquid $\bar{F}_0$ may have the form

$$\bar{F}_0 = -\int P \, d\bar{V} = -\int \left(\frac{RT}{\bar{V} - b} - \frac{a}{\bar{V}^2}\right) d\bar{V}$$

$$= -RT \ln(\bar{V} - b) - \frac{a}{\bar{V}} + \text{const.}$$

$$= N_0\left(\Theta + kT \ln \frac{n}{1 - \beta n} - \alpha n\right) \tag{6-78}$$

in which Θ is a function of T only. The Helmholtz free energy in a volume V for a homogeneous liquid at constant temperature is

$$F_0 = \int_V d\tau \left(n\Theta + nkT \ln \frac{n}{1 - \beta n} - n^2\alpha\right) = \int_V f_0 \, d\tau \tag{6-78a}$$

where

$$f_0 \left(= n\Theta + nkT \ln \frac{n}{1 - \beta n} - n^2\alpha\right)$$

is the volume density of the Helmholtz free energy in a homogeneous liquid and $d\tau$ is a volume element. The first and second derivatives of f with respect to n are

$$\frac{\partial f}{\partial n} = (\Theta + kT) + kT \ln \frac{n}{1 - \beta n} + kT \frac{\beta n}{1 - \beta n} - 2n\alpha$$

$$\frac{\partial^2 f}{\partial n^2} = \frac{kT}{n}\left[\frac{1}{(1 - \beta n)^2} - \frac{2\alpha n}{kT}\right] \tag{6-79}$$

We can relate this second derivative of f to the isothermal compressibility κ, which is defined as

$$\kappa = -\frac{1}{V}\left(\frac{\partial V}{\partial P}\right)_T$$

On differentiating $n = N/V$ we find $dV = -(V^2/N) \, dn$. So

$$\frac{1}{\kappa} = n\left(\frac{\partial P}{\partial n}\right)_T$$

With the thermodynamic relation $P = -(\partial F/\partial V)_T$ we then have

$$P = \frac{N}{V^2}\left(\frac{\partial F}{\partial n}\right)_T = n^2\left[\frac{\partial}{\partial n}\left(\frac{f}{n}\right)\right]_T = n\left(\frac{\partial f}{\partial n}\right)_T - f$$

Thus

$$\frac{1}{\kappa} = n^2\left(\frac{\partial^2 f}{\partial n^2}\right)_T$$

With (6-79) we get

$$\frac{1}{\kappa} = nkT\left[\frac{1}{(1-n\beta)^2} - \frac{2\alpha n}{kT}\right] \tag{6-80}$$

We now want to take into account the fact that in our volume the number of molecules per cubic centimeter is not constant but variable. The number density n may be represented $n_0 + v(\xi, \eta, \zeta)$, where v represents deviations from the average number of molecules per cubic centimeter, n_0. Then we get the free energy with variable density,

$$F = \int_V f \, d\tau = \int_V \left[f_0 + v\left(\frac{\partial f}{\partial n}\right)_0 + \frac{v^2}{2}\left(\frac{\partial^2 f}{\partial n^2}\right)_0 + \cdots \right] d\tau$$

in a rectangular coordinate system (ξ, η, ζ) measured from the center of the central molecule with coordinates x, y, and z. Since $\int v \, d\tau = 0$,

$$F = \int f_0 \, d\tau + \frac{1}{2}\int \left(\frac{\partial^2 f}{\partial n^2}\right)_0 v^2 \, d\tau + \cdots$$

$$= F_0 + \int \frac{1}{2\kappa}\frac{v^2 \, d\tau}{n^2} + \cdots \tag{6-81}$$

Combining relations (6-80) and (6-81) we obtain for the free energy of a van der Waals gas with variable density the general equation

$$F = F_0 + \int_V d\tau \frac{v^2}{2n^2}\left[\frac{nkT}{(1-\beta n)^2} - 2\alpha n^2\right] + \cdots \tag{6-82}$$

The subscript zero, indicating that all operations are to be carried out at the center of the central molecule, has been dropped. In (6-82) the quantity in brackets is $1/\kappa$, which can be calculated from critical parameters. Introduction of critical variables and reduced parameters in (6-80) gives the reciprocal compressibility,

$$\frac{1}{\kappa} = 6P_c\left\{\frac{4(n/n_c)}{[3-(n/n_c)]^2}\frac{T}{T_c} - \left(\frac{n}{n_c}\right)^2\right\} \tag{6-83}$$

For the sake of simplicity in the formula, we shall consider that our scattering experiment is carried out at constant volume. In other words, the density is kept equal to the critical density, or $n = n_c$; then we have

$$\frac{1}{\kappa} = 6P_c\left(\frac{T}{T_c} - 1\right) \qquad (6\text{-}83a)$$

which shows that the quantity $1/\kappa$ approaches zero as the critical temperature is approached.

B. Molecular Energy in a Medium with Variable Density (Including the Effect of Gradients of Fluctuations)

The wavelength of supersonic waves on which the scattered light can be considered as reflected goes from ∞ for $\theta = 0$ to $\lambda/2$ for $\theta = \pi$. This is exactly Bragg's relation for a series of reflecting planes at mutual distance Λ:

$$\frac{1}{\Lambda} = \frac{s}{\lambda} \qquad \text{with } s = 2\sin\frac{\theta}{2} \qquad (6\text{-}75)$$

In this way a range of frequencies going from 0 to roughly 10^4 Mc is covered. For systems in the neighborhood of the critical point, the scattered intensity at various angles represents a measurement of the square of the amplitude of thermal supersonic waves over the corresponding range of wavelengths. Einstein's formula (6-77) is equivalent to saying that the square of the amplitude of supersonic waves are the same over the whole frequency interval. This statement rests on the assumption that the potential energy involved in the propagation of sound waves is due to compressibility only, or that the work required to produce a density (or concentration) fluctuation depends only on the amplitude of the local fluctuations. However, near the critical point, the work of compression (or osmotic work) required to create a certain density (or concentration) fluctuation becomes smaller and smaller. Therefore, it becomes important to consider any other possible source of energy, even if it is unimportant under ordinary conditions. We shall first calculate the molecular energy, taking into account the gradient of the density (or concentration) fluctuations (*19*) and later see what effect it has on the scattered intensity near the critical point.

Let us assume that the potential energy between two molecules is solely a function of their mutual distance r. Recall $\varepsilon(r)$ as the interaction energy between two molecules. The potential energy of one central molecule due to the action of its surroundings is

$$E = \int n\varepsilon(r)\, d\tau$$

where in an approximation of the actual behavior the integration of r extends from the point of contact to infinity. The number of molecules per cubic centimeter in our volume is variable and can be developed in powers of the coordinates around the position of the central molecule. If we now confine our attention to the interaction between one central molecule and surrounding molecules of the same kind, we can write

$$n(x + \xi, y + \eta, z + \zeta) = n_0 + \left[\xi\left(\frac{\partial n}{\partial x}\right)_0 + \eta\left(\frac{\partial n}{\partial y}\right)_0 + \zeta\left(\frac{\partial n}{\partial z}\right)_0 \right]$$

$$+ \frac{1}{2}\left[\xi^2\left(\frac{\partial^2 n}{\partial x^2}\right)_0 + \eta^2\left(\frac{\partial^2 n}{\partial y^2}\right)_0 + \zeta^2\left(\frac{\partial^2 n}{\partial z^2}\right)_0 \right] + \cdots$$

in a coordinate system that has rectangular coordinates ξ, η, and ζ measured from the center of the central molecule with coordinates x, y, and z. For the isotropic case, $r^2 = \xi^2 + \eta^2 + \zeta^2$ and $\xi^2 = \eta^2 = \zeta^2$. Then

$$n(x + \xi, y + \eta, z + \zeta) = n_0 + \left[\xi\left(\frac{\partial n}{\partial x}\right)_0 + \cdots \right]$$

$$+ \frac{r^2}{6}\left[\left(\frac{\partial^2 n}{\partial x^2}\right)_0 + \left(\frac{\partial^2 n}{\partial y^2}\right)_0 + \left(\frac{\partial^2 n}{\partial z^2}\right)_0 \right] + \cdots \quad (6\text{-}84)$$

If we break the series off at the second power of these coordinates, the result is

$$E = n_0 \int \varepsilon(r)\, d\tau + \tfrac{1}{6}\nabla^2 n \int r^2 \varepsilon(r)\, d\tau \quad (6\text{-}85)$$

in which $d\tau$ is an element of volume, ∇^2 is the Laplacian operator calculated at the position of the central molecule, and the integration ranges over the surroundings of the central molecule. We can define a length such that

$$Wl^2 = \int r^2 \varepsilon(r)\, d\tau$$

where $W = \int \varepsilon(r)\, d\tau$ and the length l is the range of molecular forces, or the Debye interaction parameter. Remembering (1-15), we can calculate the total potential energy U_{pot} of N molecules in volume V by integrating (6-85) over the whole volume,

$$2U_{pot} = NW\left(n + \frac{l^2}{6} \nabla^2 n\right) \tag{6-86}$$

where the subscript zero has been dropped. If we write the Helmholtz free energy as

$$F = \int f \, d\tau \tag{6-78a}$$

we find now the volume density of the Helmholtz free energy, f, for a van der Waals gas with variable density is

$$f = n\Theta + nkT \ln \frac{n}{1 - \beta n} - \alpha\left(n^2 + \frac{l^2}{6} n\nabla^2 n\right) \tag{6-87}$$

in which $\alpha = -W/2 = -\frac{1}{2}\int \varepsilon(r)d\tau$. If the thermal spontaneous fluctuations of the density are relatively small, we can replace n by $n_0 + v$ and express the last term of (6-87) in terms of v. So we obtain

$$(n_0 + v)\nabla^2(n_0 + v) = (n_0 + v)\nabla^2 v = n_0\nabla^2 v + v\nabla^2 v$$

In the following formula we shall again omit the subscript zero and agree that from now on n will stand for the number of molecules per cubic centimeter in the homogeneous mixture. We remark that the volume integral over v is zero, since the origin of the coordinate system can be located at the center of mass of the system, and assume that the volume integral of $\nabla^2 v$, which is equivalent to a surface integral, gives negligible contribution. Taking all this into account, we arrive according to relation (6-82) at the result

$$F = F_0 + \int_V d\tau \left(\frac{v^2}{2n^2} \frac{1}{\kappa} - 2\alpha n^2 \frac{l^2}{6} \frac{v\nabla^2 v}{2n^2}\right) \tag{6-88}$$

where

$$\frac{1}{\kappa} = nkT\left[\frac{1}{(1 - n\beta)^2} - \frac{2\alpha n}{kT}\right]$$

as has been derived previously [Eq. (6-80)]. The periodic fluctuations in the number of molecules per cubic centimeter can be represented by

$$v = v_0 \sin(\Omega t - KX)$$

where X is a coordinate perpendicular to the reflecting wave front and is in the direction of propagation of the supersonic wave; with Bragg's relation, K is $2\pi/\Lambda = 2\pi s/\lambda$, and Ω is the angular frequency of the supersonic wave. Then

$$v^2 = v_0^2 \sin^2(\Omega t - KX)$$

$$\nabla^2 v = -v_0 K^2 \sin(\Omega t - KX)$$

$$v\nabla^2 v = -K^2 v_0^2 \sin^2(\Omega t - KX) = -K^2 v^2$$

Thus (6-88) becomes

$$F = F_0 + \int_V d\tau \, \frac{v^2}{2n^2} \left(\frac{1}{\kappa} + 2\alpha n^2 \frac{K^2 l^2}{6} \right) \tag{6-88a}$$

This differs from the previously derived equation for free energy (6-82) by substituting for $1/\kappa$ the expression $(1/\kappa) + 2\alpha n^2 (l^2/6)K^2$.

C. Light Scattering (Including the Effect of Gradients of Fluctuations)

For a gas at critical density, we have

$$\frac{1}{\kappa} = 6P_c(\tau - 1) \qquad \text{with } \tau = \frac{T}{T_c} \tag{6-83a}$$

as previously shown. Likewise we can write

$$2\alpha n_c^2 = \frac{2\alpha}{9\beta^2} = \frac{6}{27} \frac{\alpha}{\beta^2} = 6P_c$$

and therefore,

$$\frac{1}{\kappa} + 2\alpha n^2 \frac{l^2}{6} K^2 = 6P_c \left[(\tau - 1) + \frac{l^2 K^2}{6} \right]$$

$$= 6P_c \left[(\tau - 1) + \frac{4\pi^2}{6} \frac{l^2}{\lambda^2} s^2 \right]$$

Instead of Einstein's formulation,

$$\frac{I}{I_0} = \frac{k^4}{16\pi^2} \frac{\sin^2 \vartheta}{R^2} \left(\frac{\rho \, d\epsilon}{\epsilon \, d\rho} \right)^2 V \frac{\beta T}{1/\kappa} \tag{6-77}$$

we obtain a new expression which takes into account the local gradients of fluctuations due to the thermal motion of molecules,

$$\frac{I}{I_0} = \frac{k^4}{16\pi^2} \frac{\sin^2 \vartheta}{R^2} \left(\frac{\rho \, d\epsilon}{\epsilon \, d\rho} \right)^2 V \frac{\beta T}{6P_c (\tau - 1) + (4\pi^2/6)(l^2/\lambda^2)s^2} \tag{6-89}$$

s being $2 \sin(\theta/2)$.

Both (6-77) and (6-89) indicate an increase in the scattered intensity as we approach the critical point, because κ is proportional to $1/(\tau - 1)$. But (6-89) further predicts an increase in the angular dissymmetry. If

$$\frac{4\pi^2}{6}\frac{l^2}{\lambda^2}\frac{s^2}{\tau - 1} = 1$$

the scattered intensity should show a pronounced dissymmetry. With $s = 2$, $\lambda = 3000$ A, and l (range of molecular force) $= 10$ A:

$$\tau - 1 = \frac{4\pi^2}{6}\left(\frac{10}{3000}\right)^2 4 \simeq 3 \times 10^{-4}$$

Suppose $T_c = 300°K$; it would be necessary to approach the critical temperature within $0.09°C$ to establish the proposed dissymmetry.

The remarkable fact is that if the foregoing explanation is accepted, molecular interaction ranges of the order of 10 A can be measured with visible light of a wavelength of the order of 3000 A. From this viewpoint, scattering measurements on systems near the critical point are important for the study of molecular interactions.

An indication of the limitations of (6-89) can be seen by examining it in terms of the correlation function. If we use $e^{-(r/a)}/(r/a)$ as an approximate expression for the correlation function, then the scattered intensity I is proportional to

$$4\pi \int_0^\infty \frac{e^{-r/a}}{r/a}\frac{\sin ksr}{ksr}r^2\,dr = \mathscr{I}_m\left(\frac{4\pi a}{ks}\int_0^\infty e^{-r/a}e^{iksr}\,dr\right)$$

$$= \frac{4\pi a}{ks}\mathscr{I}_m\left(\frac{1}{(1/a) - iks}\right) = \frac{4\pi a^2}{ks}\mathscr{I}_m\left(\frac{1}{1 - iksa}\right)$$

$$= 4\pi a^3\frac{1}{1 + k^2s^2a^2}$$

or

$$I \propto \frac{1}{1 + (4\pi^2s^2a^2/\lambda^2)}$$

We have only to identify a^2 with $L^2/6$, L being the persistence length as previously defined in (6-60a). Now, the exponential form $e^{-(r/a)}/(r/a)$ is a good approximation for the correlation function only when r is large. As r approaches 0, $C(r)$ approaches infinity. This does not satisfy the definition of the correlation function [as $r \to 0$, $C(r) \to 1$]. Thus the intensity formula is also an approximation, only for small values of the addition $(4\pi^2/6)(s^2/\lambda^2)[l^2/(\tau - 1)]$. In the case of light scattering, s^2/λ^2 is often small enough to make (6-89) a good approximation, provided the temperature distance $(T - T_c)$ is not too small. The formula should not be extended to the small-angle X-ray scattering range, where s^2/λ^2 is much larger, without further justification.† A generalized interaction equation will be derived.

As a slight digression, we shall derive the exponential form of the approximate correlation function on the basis of a superposition of supersonic waves passing through a fluid.

A supersonic wave traveling through a homogeneous liquid induces small periodic density fluctuations, σ, which according to (6-66) can be represented by

$$\sigma = \sigma \cos(\Omega t - K(\mathbf{S} \cdot \mathbf{r}))$$

where $\mathbf{S}$ is a unit vector indicating the direction of propagation of the supersonic wave. Consider two points A and B in the liquid. The product of the two density fluctuations in points A and B is

$$\sigma_A \sigma_B = \sigma_0^2 \cos(\Omega t - K(\mathbf{S} \cdot \mathbf{r}_A))\cos(\Omega t - K(\mathbf{S} \cdot \mathbf{r}_B))$$

Since $2 \cos x \cos y = \cos(x + y) + \cos(x - y)$, we may write

$$\sigma_A \sigma_B = \frac{\sigma_0^2}{2} \cos[2\Omega t - K(\mathbf{S} \cdot (\mathbf{r}_A + \mathbf{r}_B))] + \frac{\sigma_0^2}{2} \cos K[\mathbf{S} \cdot (\mathbf{r}_B - \mathbf{r}_A)]$$

The time average of the product of the two density fluctuations in points A and B is defined as

$$\overline{\sigma_A \sigma_B} = \frac{1}{\tau} \int_0^\tau \sigma_A \sigma_B \, dt$$

where τ is a period representing a very long time. Suppose

$$Y = \frac{1}{\tau} \int_0^\tau \frac{\sigma_0^2}{2} \cos[2\Omega t - K(\mathbf{S} \cdot (\mathbf{r}_A + \mathbf{r}_B))] \, dt$$

$$= \frac{\sigma_0^2}{4\Omega\tau} \{\sin[2\Omega\tau - K(\mathbf{S} \cdot (\mathbf{r}_A + \mathbf{r}_B))] - \sin[-K(\mathbf{S} \cdot (\mathbf{r}_A + \mathbf{r}_B))]\}$$

† This extension has been used by J. E. Thomas and P. W. Schmidt in their X-ray study of critical opalescence of argon where L^2 is relatively small [*J. Chem. Phys.*, **39**, 2506 (1963)]. Note that references on experimental data serve as demonstrations and are not intended to be comprehensive.

As $\tau \to \infty$, $Y \to 0$, which reduces

$$\overline{\sigma_A \sigma_B} = \frac{\sigma_0^2}{2} \cos K(\mathbf{S} \cdot (\mathbf{r}_B - \mathbf{r}_A))$$

Now all the different thermal waves are independent of one another. Remembering that the number of waves in the interval $K^2 \, dK \, dW$ (dW being an element of the solid angle) is

$$dZ = \frac{V_s}{(2\pi)^3} K^2 \, dK \, dW \qquad (6\text{-}72)$$

we find immediately

$$\langle \sigma_A \sigma_B \rangle = \frac{V_s}{(2\pi)^3} \int \frac{\sigma_0^2}{2} \cos K(\mathbf{S} \cdot \mathbf{r}) K^2 \, dK \, dW$$

if $\mathbf{r}$ represents the vector from A to B. The integration over the solid angle can be carried out with the result

$$\langle \sigma_A \sigma_B \rangle = 4\pi \frac{V_s}{(2\pi)^3} \int_{K=0}^{K=K_m} \frac{\sigma_0^2}{2} \frac{\sin Kr}{Kr} K^2 \, dK$$

where K_m is determined by the fact that the liquid has a finite number of degrees of freedom. But the scattered intensity is proportional to σ_0, so we have

$$\langle \sigma_A \sigma_B \rangle \propto \int_0^{K_m} \frac{1}{1 + (K^2 L^2/6)} \frac{\sin Kr}{Kr} K^2 \, dK$$

with $L^2 = l^2/(\tau - 1)$ for a van der Waals gas.

If we take the upper limit of the integral to be infinity, we have

$$\langle \sigma_A \sigma_B \rangle \propto \frac{1}{r} \frac{\partial}{\partial r} \left(\int_0^\infty \frac{\cos Kr}{1 + (K^2 L^2/6)} \, dK \right)$$

or letting $a^2 = L^2/6$, we then have

$$\langle \sigma_A \sigma_B \rangle \propto \frac{1}{r} \frac{\partial}{\partial r} \left(\int_0^\infty \frac{\cos Kr}{1 + K^2 a^2} \, dK \right)$$

The integration procedure is as follows. Letting $x = Ka$, and $\rho = r/a$, we have

$$\int_0^\infty \frac{\cos Kr}{1 + K^2 a^2} \, dK = \frac{1}{a} \int_0^\infty \frac{\cos x(r/a)}{1 + x^2} \, dx$$

$$= \frac{1}{2a} \int_{-\infty}^\infty \frac{\cos \rho x}{1 + x^2} \, dx = \frac{1}{2a} \int_{-\infty}^\infty \frac{e^{i\rho x}}{1 + x^2} \, dx$$

Since

$$\frac{1}{x^2+1} = \frac{1}{2i}\left(\frac{1}{x-i} - \frac{1}{x+i}\right)$$

this gives

$$\frac{1}{2a}\int_{-\infty}^{\infty} \frac{e^{i\rho x}}{1+x^2}\,dx = \frac{1}{2a}\frac{1}{2i}\int e^{i\rho x}\left(\frac{1}{x-i} - \frac{1}{x+i}\right)dx$$

$$= \frac{1}{2a}\frac{1}{2i}\,2\pi i e^{-\rho} = \frac{\pi}{2a}\,e^{-r/a}$$

So we find

$$\langle\sigma_A\sigma_B\rangle \propto \frac{e^{-r/a}}{r/a} \qquad \text{with } a^2 = \frac{L^2}{6} = \frac{1}{6}\frac{l^2}{\tau-1}$$

This exponential approximation for the correlation function is the form assumed in the previous paragraph.

6-4. GENERALIZED INTERACTION (26)

A. Free Energy

We have considered a liquid whose density varies from point to point in an irregular way and have developed equations which approximately represent the free energy and the scattered intensity for such a liquid, taking into account only the local gradient of fluctuations in addition to the amplitude of fluctuations due to thermal motion of the molecules. We now wish to calculate these parameters for a one-component system with variable density without making the first-order approximation.

Analogous to (1-14), the potential energy of one central molecule due to surrounding molecules of the same kind is

$$E = \int n'\varepsilon(r)\,d\tau' \tag{6-90}$$

where the number density n' is a variable. Similarly, the energy density, U_{pot}/V, of the system with variable number-density fluctuations is

$$2\frac{U_{pot}}{V} = n\int n'\varepsilon(r)\,d\tau'$$

$$= n\int n\varepsilon(r)\,d\tau' - n\int (n-n')\varepsilon(r)\,d\tau' \tag{6-91}$$

If we assume that the thermal spontaneous fluctuations of the density is small, we can express the density which varies from point to point in the liquid as

$$n = n_0 + v(\xi, \eta, \zeta)$$

where n_0 is the average number of molecules per cubic centimeter and v is the fluctuation. So, according to (6-91), we have

$$2 \frac{U_{pot}}{V} = n^2 \int \varepsilon(r) \, d\tau' - (n_0 + v) \int (v - v')\varepsilon(r) \, d\tau'$$

Using our previous definitions of $W [= \int \varepsilon(r) \, d\tau]$ and $\alpha (= -W/2)$, we get

$$\frac{U_{pot}}{V} = -\alpha \left[n^2 + \frac{(n_0 + v) \int (v' - v)\varepsilon(r) \, d\tau'}{\int \varepsilon(r) \, d\tau'} \right] \tag{6-92}$$

In order to connect the density fluctuations with the scattered intensity observable at a definite angle, say θ, between the scattered and the primary ray, it is once again advantageous to make a Fourier analysis of the local fluctuations. For a definite angle θ characterized by $s [= 2 \sin(\theta/2)]$, only the wave of the wavelength Λ, connected with the wavelength of the light by Bragg's relation

$$\frac{1}{\Lambda} = \frac{s}{\lambda} \tag{6-75}$$

is responsible for the scattering. So we shall concentrate on this angle and let v be

$$v = v_0 \sin(\Omega t - KX) = v_0 \sin \psi$$

where X is the direction of propagation of the supersonic waves, $K = 2\pi/\Lambda$, and Ω is the angular frequency of the supersonic wave. Similarly,

$$v' = v_0 \sin(\Omega t - K(X + \xi)) = v_0 \sin(\psi - K\xi)$$

with ξ, η, and ζ the rectangular coordinates measured from the center of the central molecule. We then have

$$v' - v = v_0 \sin(\psi - K\xi) - v_0 \sin \psi$$
$$= v_0[\sin \psi \cos K\xi - \cos \psi \sin K\xi] - v_0 \sin \psi$$
$$= -v_0 \sin \psi[1 - \cos K\xi] - v_0 \cos \psi \sin K\xi$$

Now let us consider the integral $\int (v' - v)\varepsilon(r) \, d\tau'$ which appears in (6-92). The integration with respect to the angle can be performed, since we still assume that the mutual potential energy of interaction $\varepsilon(r)$ depends only on r. First of all, we can make the evaluations

$$\int \cos(K\xi)\,dW$$

$$= \int_0^\pi \cos(Kr\cos\phi)\,\frac{\sin\phi}{2}\,d\phi$$

$$= -\frac{1}{Kr}\int_0^{\pi/2} \cos(Kr\cos\phi)\,d(Kr\cos\phi)$$

$$= \frac{\sin Kr}{Kr}$$

and

$$\int \sin(K\xi)\,dW = 0$$

So we have

$$\int (v'-v)\varepsilon(r)\,d\tau' = -v_0\sin\psi\int\left(1-\frac{\sin Kr}{Kr}\right)\varepsilon(r)\,d\tau'$$

Proceeding with the evaluation of (6-92) we can now write

$$v\int (v'-v)\varepsilon(r)\,d\tau' = -v_0^2\sin^2\psi\int\left(1-\frac{\sin Kr}{Kr}\right)\varepsilon(r)\,d\tau'$$

or

$$v\int (v'-v)\varepsilon(r)\,d\tau' = -v^2\int\left(1-\frac{\sin Kr}{Kr}\right)\varepsilon(r)d\tau'$$

The integral $n_0\int (v'-v)\varepsilon(r)\,d\tau'$ will vanish when we perform the integration over the whole volume to establish the value of the Helmholtz free energy F.

Now we have, in terms of n,

$$f = n\Theta + nkT\ln\frac{n}{1-\beta n} - \alpha\left[n^2 + \frac{n\int (n'-n)\varepsilon(r)\,d\tau'}{\int\varepsilon(r)\,d\tau'}\right]$$

where $f_0 = n\Theta + nkT\ln[n/(1-\beta n)] - n^2\alpha$ [Eq. (6-78a)]. With the use of our development of (6-92) this gives

$$F = F_0 + \int d\tau\,\frac{v^2}{2n^2}\left(\frac{1}{\kappa} + 2\alpha n^2 Q\right) \tag{6-93}$$

in which

$$Q = \frac{\int \varepsilon(r)[1 - (\sin Kr/Kr)] \, d\tau'}{\int \varepsilon(r) \, d\tau'}$$

Equation (6-93) is our generalized expression for the free energy of a one-component system with variable density. This differs from the previous equation for free energy with variable density, which took into account only the additional local gradient of density fluctuations (6-88a). By substitution for $(1/\kappa) + 2\alpha n^2 K^2(l^2/6)$ in (6-88a) the expression

$$\frac{1}{\kappa} + 2\alpha n^2 \frac{\int \varepsilon(r)[1 - (\sin Kr/Kr)] \, d\tau'}{\int \varepsilon(r) \, d\tau'}$$

we get (6-93).

B. Light Scattering (with Generalized Interaction)

For the intensity of light scattered at an angle θ (between secondary and primary ray) at a large distance R from a scattering volume V, Einstein's theory gives a result which can be formulated in the form (for unpolarized light)

$$\frac{I}{I_0} = \frac{k^4}{16\pi^2} \frac{1 + \cos^2 \theta}{2} \frac{V}{R^2} \left(\frac{\rho \, d\varepsilon}{\varepsilon \, d\rho}\right)^2 \frac{\beta T}{1/\kappa} \tag{6-77}$$

The classical scattering formula can immediately be corrected for the effect of the energy connected with molecular interactions by writing, instead of (6-77),

$$\frac{I}{I_0} = \frac{k^4}{16\pi^2} \frac{1 + \cos^2 \theta}{2} \frac{V}{R^2} \left(\frac{\rho \, d\varepsilon}{\varepsilon \, d\rho}\right)^2 \frac{\beta T}{(1/\kappa) + 2\alpha n^2 Q} \tag{6-94}$$

with

$$Q = \frac{\int \varepsilon(r)[1 - (\sin Kr/Kr)] \, d\tau'}{\int \varepsilon(r) \, d\tau'}$$

If the experiment is carried out at $n = n_c$, and we again assume the behavior of a van der Waals gas, $(1/\kappa) + 2\alpha n^2$ may be represented by the expression $6P_c[(\tau - 1) + 1]$. Then we have

$$\frac{I}{I_0} = \frac{k^4}{16\pi^2} \frac{1 + \cos^2 \theta}{2} \frac{V}{R^2} \left(\frac{\rho \, d\varepsilon}{\varepsilon \, d\rho}\right)^2 \frac{\beta T}{6P_c} \frac{1}{(\tau - 1) + Q}$$

From a detailed measurement of angular dependence of scattered intensity, it is now *possible* to obtain further information on the form of the mutual potential energy of interaction of two molecules, $\varepsilon(r)$, as a function of their separation distance by means of a mathematical transformation.

We shall briefly consider the function $Q(K)$ in (6-93):

1. If we approximate $\sin Kr / Kr$ by its first two terms we obtain the old approximation

$$F = F_0 + \int d\tau \, \frac{v^2}{2n^2} \left(\frac{1}{\kappa} + 2\alpha n^2 \frac{K^2 l^2}{6} \right) \tag{6-88a}$$

2. If we accept for the interaction

$$\varepsilon(r) = - \varepsilon_0 \left(\frac{2a}{r} \right)^6$$

with $2a$ as the diameter of the molecule, we have

$$Q = 1 - \frac{3}{4\gamma} \left(\sin \gamma + \frac{\gamma}{3} \cos \gamma - \frac{\gamma^2}{6} \sin \gamma - \frac{\gamma^3}{6} \cos \gamma + \frac{\gamma^4}{6} \int_1^\infty \frac{\sin \gamma x}{x} \, dx \right)$$

where $\gamma = 2aK$. The approximation for small γ can be obtained by evaluating the integral:

$$\int_1^\infty \frac{\sin \gamma x}{x} \, dx = \int_0^\infty \frac{\sin \gamma x}{x} \, dx - \int_0^1 \frac{\sin \gamma x}{x} \, dx$$

$$= \frac{\pi}{2} - \gamma + \frac{\gamma^3}{18} - \frac{\gamma^5}{600} + \cdots$$

It turns out that for small and large values of $\gamma \, (= 2aK)$,

$$Q \simeq \frac{\gamma^2}{2} - \frac{\pi}{16} \gamma^3 + \frac{\gamma^4}{40} + \cdots \qquad \text{for } \gamma \ll 1$$

$$\simeq 1 - \frac{3 \cos \gamma}{\gamma^2} + \cdots \qquad \text{for } \gamma \gg 1$$

Under these circumstances our molecular interaction parameter, l, is given by the relation $l^2 = 12a^2$.

6-5. POTENTIAL ENERGY AND FREE ENERGY OF TWO-COMPONENT SYSTEMS WITH CONSTANT COMPOSITION (WITHOUT COMPOSITION FLUCTUATIONS) (27)

Let us prepare a mixture of two liquids 1 and 2 by mixing N_1 molecules of kind 1 with N_2 molecules of kind 2. We shall assume that any possible contraction in mixing at constant temperature and pressure is negligible. Then we may express volume fractions as

$$\phi_1 = \frac{n_1\omega_1}{n_1\omega_1 + n_2\omega_2} = n_1\omega_2 = \frac{N_1\omega_1}{N_1\omega_1 + N_2\omega_2}$$

$$\phi_2 = \frac{n_2\omega_2}{n_1\omega_1 + n_2\omega_2} = n_2\omega_2 = \frac{N_2\omega_2}{N_1\omega_1 + N_2\omega_2} \tag{6-95}$$

where ω_1 ($= V_1/N_1$) and ω_2 ($= V_2/N_2$) are not the actual volumes occupied by one molecule of kind 1 and of kind 2, respectively, but they are the partial molecular volumes; n_1 and n_2 are the corresponding number of molecules per cubic centimeter. We further assume that the interaction between two molecules depends only on the separation distance between their centers, r. Let $\varepsilon_{ij}(r)$ be the potential energy between molecule i and molecule j. The potential energy u_1 of one molecule of kind 1 due to surrounding molecules is the sum of potential energies of interaction of one molecule of kind 1 due to surrounding molecules of the same kind and of potential energies of interaction of this central molecule due to surrounding molecules of the second kind:

$$u_1 = n_1 \int \varepsilon_{11}\, d\tau + n_2 \int \varepsilon_{12}\, d\tau$$

in which $d\tau$ is an element of volume and the integration ranges over the surroundings of the central molecule. Similarly, for a molecule of kind 2 the potential energy due to surrounding molecules is

$$u_2 = n_1 \int \varepsilon_{21}\, d\tau + n_2 \int \varepsilon_{22}\, d\tau$$

If we let $\int \varepsilon_{ij}\, d\tau = W_{ij}$, then

$$u_1 = n_1 W_{11} + n_2 W_{12} \qquad u_2 = n_1 W_{21} + n_2 W_{22} \tag{6-96}$$

W_{ij} has the dimension of energy times volume. The total potential energy U contained in our mixture of N_1 molecules of kind 1 and N_2 molecules of kind 2 is

$$2U = N_1(n_1 W_{11} + n_2 W_{12}) + N_2(n_1 W_{21} + n_2 W_{22})$$

With the use of volume fractions ϕ_1 and ϕ_2 we can now express the potential energy contained in our mixture by

$$2U = N_1\left(\frac{W_{11}}{\omega_1}\phi_1 + \frac{W_{12}}{\omega_2}\phi_2\right) + N_2\left(\frac{W_{21}}{\omega_1}\phi_1 + \frac{W_{22}}{\omega_2}\phi_2\right) \tag{6-97}$$

According to (1-15) the total potential energy, U_{pure}, of two separate liquids is

$$2U_{\text{pure}} = N_1 \frac{W_{11}}{\omega_1} + N_2 \frac{W_{22}}{\omega_2} \tag{6-98}$$

The difference between (6-98) and (6-97) is the excess energy of the mixture over that of the two separate components, and comes out to be

$$-2(U - U_{\text{pure}}) = N_1 \left(\frac{W_{11}}{\omega_1} \phi_2 - \frac{W_{12}}{\omega_2} \phi_2 \right) + N_2 \left(\frac{W_{22}}{\omega_2} \phi_1 - \frac{W_{21}}{\omega_1} \phi_1 \right) \tag{6-99}$$

Since $W_{12} = W_{21}$ we have

$$U - U_{\text{pure}} = -V \frac{\phi_1 \phi_2}{2} \left(\frac{W_{11}}{\omega_1^2} + \frac{W_{22}}{\omega_2^2} - 2 \frac{W_{12}}{\omega_1 \omega_2} \right) \tag{6-100}$$

V being the volume occupied by the liquid mixture. An interpretation of this relation can be made by using van Laar's postulate, $W_{12} = (W_{11}W_{22})^{1/2}$, which gives us

$$U - U_{\text{pure}} = -V \frac{\phi_1 \phi_2}{2} \left[\left(\frac{W_{11}}{\omega_1^2} \right)^{1/2} - \left(\frac{W_{22}}{\omega_2^2} \right)^{1/2} \right]^2$$

The square of a number is always positive, so to mix the two liquids we would have to furnish energy. However, we must remember that this conclusion is based on the postulate that $W_{12} = (W_{11}W_{22})^{1/2}$, which does not always hold.

With our expression for the excess potential energy (6-100) we can now calculate the excess Helmholtz free energy of the homogeneous mixture. For the entropy change, $S - S_{\text{pure}}$, which occurs in going from the two separate liquids to the mixture, we shall assume the formulation

$$S - S_{\text{pure}} = -k \int (n_1 \ln \phi_1 + n_2 \ln \phi_2) \, d\tau \tag{6-101}$$

in which k is the Boltzmann constant. Relation (6-101), which contains volume fractions instead of the classical mole fractions, seems to be a better representation of facts, especially for the case in which one of the components is a polymer. Since $n_1 = \phi_1/\omega_1$ and $n_2 = \phi_2/\omega_2$, we shall prefer for the formulation of the excess entropy of mixing the relation

$$S - S_{\text{pure}} = -k \int \left[\left(\frac{\phi_1}{\omega_1} \right) \ln \phi_1 + \left(\frac{\phi_2}{\omega_2} \right) \ln \phi_2 \right] d\tau \tag{6-102}$$

For the excess free energy of the mixture over that of the two separate components, we now have

$$\frac{F_0}{kT} = \frac{(U - U_{\text{pure}}) - T(S - S_{\text{pure}})}{kT}$$

$$= \int \left[\frac{\phi_1}{\omega_1} \ln \phi_1 + \frac{\phi_2}{\omega_2} \ln \phi_2 - \frac{\Omega}{2kT} \phi_1 \phi_2 \right] d\tau = \int \frac{f_0}{kT} d\tau \quad (6\text{-}103)$$

with $\Omega = (W_{11}/\omega_1^2) + (W_{22}/\omega_2^2) - 2(W_{12}/\omega_1\omega_2)$. Note that F_0 is the excess free energy of the *homogeneous* mixture.

6-6. CLASSICAL COMPOSITION FLUCTUATIONS

For small thermal spontaneous composition fluctuations, the variations in volume fractions, ϕ_1 and ϕ_2, can be represented by one single variable η such that

$$\phi_1 = \phi_1^0 + \eta \quad \text{and} \quad \phi_2 = \phi_2^0 - \eta \quad (6\text{-}104)$$

where ϕ_1^0 and ϕ_2^0 are the volume fractions of components 1 and 2, respectively, in the perfectly homogeneous mixture. Note that $\phi_1 + \phi_2 = \phi_1^0 + \phi_2^0 = 1$. Equation (6-104) will also make the integral of η over the volume of the mixture equal to zero.

We can express the volume density of the Helmholtz free energy f as a series arranged in powers of η. Retaining only terms up to the second power, we obtain

$$\frac{F}{kT} = \int \left(\frac{\phi_1}{\omega_1} \ln \phi_1 + \frac{\phi_2}{\omega_2} \ln \phi_2 - \frac{\Omega}{2kT} \phi_1 \phi_2 \right) d\tau$$

$$= \int \left[\frac{\phi_1^0 + \eta}{\omega_1} \ln(\phi_1^0 + \eta) + \frac{\phi_2^0 - \eta}{\omega_2} \ln(\phi_2^0 - \eta) - \frac{\Omega}{2kT} (\phi_1^0 + \eta)(\phi_2^0 - \eta) \right] d\tau$$

$$\simeq \int \left\{ \left(\frac{\phi_1^0}{\omega_1} \ln \phi_1^0 + \frac{\phi_2^0}{\omega_2} \ln \phi_2^0 - \frac{\Omega}{2kT} \phi_1^0 \phi_2^0 \right) \right.$$

$$+ \left[\frac{1}{\omega_1} (1 + \ln \phi_1^0) - \frac{1}{\omega_2} (1 + \ln \phi_2^0) - \frac{\Omega}{2kT} (\phi_2^0 - \phi_1^0) \right] \eta$$

$$\left. + \left(\frac{1}{\omega_2 \phi_1^0} + \frac{1}{\omega_2 \phi_2^0} + \frac{\Omega}{kT} \right) \frac{\eta^2}{2} \right\} d\tau$$

$$= \frac{F_0}{kT} + \int \left(\frac{1}{\omega_1 \phi_1^0} + \frac{1}{\omega_2 \phi_2^0} + \frac{\Omega}{kT} \right) \frac{\eta^2}{2} d\tau \quad (6\text{-}105)$$

From now on we shall leave out the superscript zero and agree that ϕ_1 and ϕ_2 represent the volume fractions in the homogeneous mixture. Accepting for a homogeneous mixture the formulation

$$\frac{F_0}{kT} = N_1 \ln \phi_1 + N_2 \ln \phi_2 - \frac{\Omega}{2kT} \frac{N_1\omega_1 N_2\omega_2}{N_1\omega_1 + N_2\omega_2}$$

which corresponds to (6-103), we derive (by partial differentiation with respect to N_1)† an expression for the excess chemical potential of this component 1, ψ_1:

$$\frac{\psi_1}{kT} = \ln(1 - \phi_2) + \left(1 - \frac{1}{x}\right)\phi_2 - \left(\frac{\Omega}{2kT}\right)\omega_1\phi_2^2 \qquad (6\text{-}106)$$

in which x stands for the quotient ω_2/ω_1. According to the usual thermodynamic rules, the quantity ψ_1/kT is equal to the negative product of osmotic pressure P^* divided by kT and the volume ω_1 "occupied" by one molecule of component 1. Hence

$$\frac{P^*\omega_1}{kT} = -\ln(1 - \phi_2) - \left(1 - \frac{1}{x}\right)\phi_2 + \left(\frac{\Omega}{2kT}\right)\omega_1\phi_2^2 \qquad (6\text{-}107)$$

According to (6-107), the curve which represents the osmotic pressure as a function of the volume fraction of the second component depends strongly on the parameter Ω/kT. By differentiating (6-107) twice with respect to ϕ_2 and equating the first and the second differential quotient

---

† Partial differentiation of F_0 with respect to N_1: The excess chemical potential of component 1, ψ_1, may be defined as

$$\psi_1 = \left(\frac{\partial \Delta G}{\partial N_1}\right)_{T,P,N_2} = \left(\frac{\partial \Delta F}{\partial N_1}\right)_{T,P,N_2} + P\left(\frac{\partial \Delta V}{\partial N_1}\right)_{T,P,N_2}$$

where G is the Gibbs free energy. Since we have assumed negligible change in volume for our mixing process, $\Delta G \simeq \Delta F$. Thus

$$\frac{\psi_1}{kT} = \left(\frac{\partial(F_0/kT)}{\partial N_1}\right)_{T,P,N_2} = \ln \phi_1 + N_1\left(\frac{1}{N_1} - \frac{\omega_1}{N_1\omega_1 + N_2\omega_2}\right)$$

$$- \frac{N_2\omega_1}{N_1\omega_1 + N_2\omega_2} - \frac{\Omega}{2kT}\left[\frac{\omega_1 N_2\omega_2}{N_1\omega_1 + N_2\omega_2} - \frac{\omega_1 N_1\omega_1 N_2\omega_2}{(N_1\omega_1 + N_2\omega_2)^2}\right]$$

$$= \ln(1 - \phi_2) + 1 - \phi_1 - \frac{\omega_1}{\omega_2}\phi_2 - \frac{\Omega}{2kT}\omega_1\phi_2(1 - \phi_1)$$

$$= \ln(1 - \phi_2) + \left(1 - \frac{1}{x}\right)\phi_2 - \frac{\Omega}{2kT}\omega_1\phi_2^2 \qquad (6\text{-}106)$$

with $x = \omega_2/\omega_1$.

each to zero, we find that the curve has an inflection point with a horizontal tangent:

$$\left(\frac{\omega_1\Omega}{kT}\right)_{\text{crit}} = -\left(1 + \frac{1}{x^{1/2}}\right)^2 \tag{6-108}$$

and

$$(\phi_2)_{\text{crit}} = \frac{1}{1 + x^{1/2}} \tag{6-109}$$

Equations (6-108) and (6-109) define the critical solution temperature and the critical volume fraction of the second component in accordance with the formulation (6-103) for the free energy. Below the critical solution temperature there are two phases in contact with each other.

From (6-107) it follows that

$$\frac{1}{\phi_2}\frac{\partial}{\partial\phi_2}\left(\frac{P^*}{kT}\right) = \frac{1}{\omega_1\phi_1} + \frac{1}{\omega_2\phi_2} + \frac{\Omega}{kT}$$

so that (6-105) becomes

$$\frac{F}{kT} = \frac{F_0}{kT} + \frac{1}{kT}\int\frac{1}{\phi_2}\frac{\partial P^*}{\partial\phi_2}\frac{\eta^2}{2}\,d\tau$$

or

$$F = F_0 + \int\left(\phi_2\frac{\partial P^*}{\partial\phi_2}\right)\frac{\eta^2}{2\phi_2^2}\,d\tau \tag{6-110}$$

in which F_0 stands for the free energy of the homogeneous mixture.

In the case of density fluctuations, we had

$$F = F_0 + \frac{1}{2}\int\left(\rho\frac{\partial P}{\partial\rho}\right)\left(\frac{v}{n}\right)^2\,d\tau \tag{6-81}$$

with $\rho(\partial P/\partial\rho) = 1/\kappa$, whereas for concentration fluctuations we have [since $\phi_2(\partial P^*/\partial\phi_2) = C(\partial P^*/\partial C)$]

$$F = F_0 + \frac{1}{2}\int\left(C\frac{\partial P^*}{\partial C}\right)\left(\frac{\eta}{\phi_2}\right)^2\,d\tau \tag{6-111}$$

Now, for the intensity of light scattered at an angle θ (between the secondary and the primary ray) at a large distance R from a scattering volume V, Einstein's theory gives a result which can be formulated in the following forms:

1. For density fluctuations,

$$\frac{I}{I_0} = \frac{\pi^2}{\lambda^4} \frac{V}{R^2} \sin^2 \vartheta \left(\frac{\rho}{\epsilon} \frac{d\epsilon}{d\rho}\right)^2 \frac{kT}{\rho(dP/d\rho)} \tag{6-77}$$

2. For concentration fluctuations,

$$\frac{I}{I_0} = \frac{\pi^2}{\lambda^4} \frac{V}{R^2} \sin^2 \vartheta \left(\frac{C}{\epsilon} \frac{d\epsilon}{dC}\right)^2 \frac{kT}{C(dP^*/dC)} \tag{6-112}$$

where I and I_0 are the scattered and primary intensities, P and P^* are the hydrostatic and osmotic pressures, λ is the wavelength in the medium, C is the concentration of the second component, ϵ is the dielectric constant, and it is assumed that the primary light is polarized. For unpolarized light it is only necessary to replace $\sin^2 \vartheta$ by the term $(1 + \cos^2 \theta)/2$.

In case 1 we found that with van der Waals' equation,

$$\frac{1}{\kappa} = \rho \frac{dP}{d\rho} = 6P_c \left\{ \frac{4\rho/\rho_c}{[3 - (\rho/\rho_c)]^2} \tau - \left(\frac{\rho}{\rho_c}\right)^2 \right\}$$

and that for experiments at $\rho = \rho_c$,

$$\left(\rho \frac{dP}{d\rho}\right)_{\rho=\rho_c} = 6P_c(\tau - 1) \tag{6-83a}$$

This yields the scattering formula (for unpolarized light)

$$\frac{I}{I_0} = \frac{4\pi^2}{\lambda^4} \frac{V}{R^2} \frac{1 + \cos^2 \theta}{2} \left(\frac{\rho}{\epsilon} \frac{d\epsilon}{d\rho}\right)^2 \frac{kT}{6P_c(\tau - 1)}$$

In case 2, if we use Hildebrand's formulation for mixtures, we have

$$\left(C \frac{dP^*}{dC}\right)_{C=C_{crit}} = \frac{kT_c}{\omega_2}(\tau - 1) \dagger$$

† Evaluation of $\partial P^*/\partial \phi_2$ at the critical solution concentration:

$$\frac{1}{\phi_2} \frac{\partial}{\partial \phi_2} \left(\frac{P^*}{kT}\right) = \frac{1}{\omega_1 \phi_1} + \frac{1}{\omega_2 \phi_2} + \frac{\Omega}{kT}$$

$$\phi_2 \frac{\partial P^*}{\partial \phi_2} = \phi_2^2 kT \left(\frac{1}{\omega_1 \phi_1} + \frac{1}{\omega_2 \phi_2} + \frac{\Omega}{kT}\right)$$

At the critical solution concentration,

$$\phi_1 = \frac{1}{1 + (1/x^{1/2})} \qquad \phi_2 = \frac{1/x^{1/2}}{1 + (1/x^{1/2})} \qquad \frac{\Omega}{kT_c} = -\frac{1}{\omega_1}\left(1 + \frac{1}{x^{1/2}}\right)^2$$

and therefore the scattering formula (for unpolarized light):

$$\frac{I}{I_0} = \frac{\pi^2}{\lambda^4} \frac{V}{R^2} \frac{1 + \cos^2 \theta}{2} \left(\frac{C}{\epsilon} \frac{d\epsilon}{dC}\right)^2 \omega_2 \frac{\tau}{\tau - 1} \tag{6-113}$$

We shall now take into account the angular dissymmetry of the critical opalescence in liquid mixtures.

6-7. ANGULAR DISSYMMETRY OF CRITICAL OPALESCENCE IN LIQUID MIXTURES

We have discussed in previous sections the reason for the angular dissymmetry of the strong scattered intensity which can be observed for a one-component system in the vicinity of the critical point. It was shown that, in the first approximation, the work necessary to establish a density fluctuation depends not only on the average square of the amplitude, but also on the average square of the local gradient of that fluctuation. Under ordinary conditions the additional term in the work is very small as compared with the term which represents an effect measured by compressibility. However, in the vicinity of the critical point the compressibility gets very large, and therefore the compression work necessary to create a given amplitude of the density fluctuation becomes very small. Under these special conditions, the term proportional to the square of the local gradient becomes important.

We shall consider concentration fluctuations in the vicinity of the critical mixing point, where the square of the local gradient of concentration fluctuation becomes important. In a volume V, the number of molecules

---

By substitution, it follows that

$$\phi_2 \frac{\partial P^*}{\partial \phi_2} = \frac{\phi_2^2 kT}{\omega_1} \left(1 + \frac{1}{x^{1/2}}\right)^2 \left(1 - \frac{T_c}{T}\right)$$

$$= \frac{kT}{x\omega_1} \left(1 - \frac{T_c}{T}\right)$$

$$= \frac{kT}{\omega_2} \left(1 - \frac{T_c}{T}\right)$$

$$= \frac{kT_c}{\omega_2} (\tau - 1) \qquad \text{Q.E.D.}$$

where $\tau = T/T_c$.

per cubic centimeter is not constant but variable. From (6-84) and (6-85) we know that

$$n = n_0 + \left[\xi \left(\frac{\partial n}{\partial x} \right)_0 + \cdots \right] + \frac{1}{2} \left[\xi^2 \left(\frac{\partial^2 n}{\partial x^2} \right)_0 + \cdots \right] + \cdots$$

and that the potential energy E_{11} from one molecule of kind 1 and surrounding molecules of the same kind is

$$E_{11} = \int \varepsilon_{11} n_1 \, d\tau = n_1^0 \int \varepsilon_{11} \, d\tau + \tfrac{1}{6}(\nabla^2 n_1)_0 \int r^2 \varepsilon_{11} \, d\tau \qquad (6\text{-}114)$$

We shall indicate the integral $\int \varepsilon_{11} \, d\tau$ by W_{11} and characterize the second by introducing a length l_{11} defined as

$$l_{11}^2 W_{11} = \int r^2 \varepsilon_{11} \, d\tau \qquad (6\text{-}115)$$

We can apply the same kind of reasoning to a central molecule, again of kind 1 but now interacting with molecules of kind 2; and also to a central molecule of kind 2 interacting either with molecules of kind 1 or kind 2. For the potential energies involved in these cases, we will have the relations

$$E_{11} = W_{11}\left[n_1 + \left(\frac{l_{11}^2}{6} \right) \nabla^2 n_1 \right]$$

$$E_{12} = W_{12}\left[n_2 + \left(\frac{l_{12}^2}{6} \right) \nabla^2 n_2 \right]$$

$$E_{21} = W_{21}\left[n_1 + \left(\frac{l_{21}^2}{6} \right) \nabla^2 n_1 \right]$$

$$E_{22} = W_{22}\left[n_2 + \left(\frac{l_{22}^2}{6} \right) \nabla^2 n_2 \right]$$

in which we have left out the superscript zero since all operations are to be carried out at the center of the central molecule. It is clear that

$$W_{12} = W_{21} \qquad \text{and} \qquad l_{12}^2 = l_{21}^2$$

We can express twice the total potential energy U contained in our mixture by the formula

$$2U = \int [n_1(E_{11} + E_{12}) + n_2(E_{21} + E_{22})] \, d\tau \qquad (6\text{-}116)$$

in which $d\tau$ now indicates an element of space in the volume of our mixture. Substituting the values of the separate individual energies E_{ij} in (6-116) and again introducing the volume fraction ϕ, we get

$$2U = \int d\tau \left[\frac{W_{11}}{\omega_1^2} \phi_1^2 + \frac{W_{22}}{\omega_2^2} \phi_2^2 + 2 \frac{W_{12}}{\omega_1 \omega_2} \phi_1 \phi_2 \right]$$

$$+ \frac{1}{6} \int d\tau \left[\frac{W_{11}}{\omega_1^2} l_{11}^2 \phi_1 \nabla^2 \phi_1 + \frac{W_{22}}{\omega_2^2} l_{22}^2 \phi_2 \nabla^2 \phi_2 \right.$$

$$+ \frac{W_{12}}{\omega_1 \omega_2} l_{12}^2 (\phi_1 \nabla^2 \phi_2 + \phi_2 \nabla^2 \phi_1) \qquad (6\text{-}116a)$$

According to (6-98) we may write for U_{pure} of the two separate components before mixing,

$$2U_{\text{pure}} = \int \left[\phi_1 \left(\frac{W_{11}}{\omega_1^2} \right) + \phi_2 \left(\frac{W_{22}}{\omega_2^2} \right) \right] d\tau \qquad (6\text{-}98a)$$

The difference between (6-116a) and (6-98a) is the excess energy of the mixture over the two separate components and comes out to be

$$-(U - U_{\text{pure}}) = \int d\tau \left\{ \left(\frac{W_{11}}{\omega_1^2} + \frac{W_{22}}{\omega_2^2} - 2 \frac{W_{12}}{\omega_1 \omega_2} \right) \frac{\phi_1 \phi_2}{2} \right.$$

$$- \frac{1}{12} \left[\frac{W_{11}}{\omega_1^2} l_{11}^2 \phi_1 \nabla^2 \phi_1 + \frac{W_{22}}{\omega_2^2} l_{22}^2 \phi_2 \nabla^2 \phi_2 \right.$$

$$+ \frac{W_{12}}{\omega_1 \omega_2} l_{12}^2 (\phi_1 \nabla^2 \phi_2 + \phi_2 \nabla^2 \phi_1) \right] \right\} \qquad (6\text{-}117)$$

It remains only to combine the expression for the entropy from (6-102) and that for the energy from (6-117). We now obtain

$$\frac{F}{kT} - \frac{(U - U_{\text{pure}}) - T(S - S_{\text{pure}})}{kT} = \int d\tau (\Phi + \Phi^*) \qquad (6\text{-}118)$$

with

$$\Phi = \frac{\phi_1}{\omega_1} \ln \phi_1 + \frac{\phi_2}{\omega_2} \ln \phi_2 - \frac{1}{2kT} \left(\frac{W_{11}}{\omega_1^2} + \frac{W_{22}}{\omega_2^2} - 2 \frac{W_{12}}{\omega_1 \omega_2} \right) \phi_1 \phi_2$$

$$\Phi^* = \frac{1}{12kT} \left[\frac{W_{11}}{\omega_1^2} l_{11}^2 \phi_1 \nabla^2 \phi_1 + \frac{W_{22}}{\omega_2^2} l_{22}^2 \phi_2 \nabla^2 \phi_2 \right.$$

$$+ \frac{W_{12}}{\omega_1 \omega_2} l_{12}^2 (\phi_1 \nabla^2 \phi_2 + \phi_2 \nabla^2 \phi_1) \right]$$

The quantity Φ^* represents the contribution to the free energy of the local composition gradients.

Following Section (6-6) we represent composition fluctuations due to thermal motion of molecules by

$$\phi_1 = \phi_1^0 + \eta \qquad \phi_2 = \phi_2^0 - \eta \qquad (6\text{-}104)$$

in which ϕ_1^0 and ϕ_2^0 are volume fractions in the perfectly homogeneous mixture. So we obtain

$$\Phi = \left[\frac{\phi_1^0}{\omega_1}\ln\phi_1^0 + \frac{\phi_2^0}{\omega_2}\ln\phi_2^0 - \frac{\Omega}{2kT}\phi_1^0\phi_2^0\right]$$

$$+ \left[\frac{1}{\omega_1}(1+\ln\phi_1^0) - \frac{1}{\omega_2}(1+\ln\phi_2^0) - \frac{\Omega}{2kT}(\phi_2^0-\phi_1^0)\right]\eta$$

$$+ \left(\frac{1}{\omega_1\phi_1^0} + \frac{1}{\omega_2\phi_2^0} + \frac{\Omega}{kT}\right)\frac{\eta^2}{2}$$

$$\Phi^* = \frac{1}{2kT}\left[\left(\frac{W_{11}}{\omega_1^2}l_{11}^2 - \frac{W_{12}}{\omega_1\omega_2}l_{12}^2\right)\phi_1^0 - \left(\frac{W_{22}}{\omega_2^2}l_{22}^2 - \frac{W_{21}}{\omega_1\omega_2}l_{21}^2\right)\phi_2^0\right]\nabla^2\eta$$

$$+ \frac{H}{2kT}\eta\nabla^2\eta \qquad (6\text{-}119)$$

with the abbreviations

$$\Omega = \frac{W_{11}}{\omega_1^2} + \frac{W_{22}}{\omega_2^2} - 2\frac{W_{12}}{\omega_1\omega_2}$$

$$H = \frac{1}{6}\left(\frac{W_{11}}{\omega_1^2}l_{11}^2 + \frac{W_{22}}{\omega_2^2}l_{22}^2 - 2\frac{W_{12}}{\omega_1\omega_2}l_{12}^2\right)$$

The terms higher than η^2 have been neglected. We shall leave out the superscript zero and again agree that from now on ϕ_1 and ϕ_2 will stand for the volume fractions in the homogeneous mixture.

With reasons analogous in the derivation of (6-88), we remark that the volume integrals of both η and $\nabla^2\eta$ are dropped out. By partial differentiation, we can make the substitution

$$\int_V \eta\nabla^2\eta\,d\tau = -\int_V \text{grad}^2\eta\,d\tau + \int_S \eta\nabla\eta\cdot d\mathbf{S}$$

which is the divergence theorem. We again ignore the second integral on the right side as a possible contribution of the surface, a feature we are not interested in here. Thus we finally arrive according to (6-118) and (6-119) at the result

$$\frac{F}{kT} = \int d\tau \left[\left(\frac{\phi_1}{\omega_1} \ln \phi_1 + \frac{\phi_2}{\omega_2} \ln \phi_2 - \frac{\Omega}{2kT} \phi_1 \phi_2 \right) \right.$$

$$\left. + \left(\frac{1}{\omega_1 \phi_1} + \frac{1}{\omega_2 \phi_2} + \frac{\Omega}{kT} \right) \frac{\eta^2}{2} - \frac{H}{2kT} \text{grad}^2 \, \eta \right] \qquad (6\text{-}120)$$

In terms of Brillouin's interpretation, only one supersonic wave of wavelength Λ is responsible for the scattered intensity in a definite direction θ. The wavelength Λ of the supersonic waves obeys Bragg's relation,

$$\frac{1}{\Lambda} = \frac{s}{\lambda}$$

Considering only this special direction we can substitute for η the representation

$$\eta = \eta_0 \sin 2\pi \left(\frac{X}{\Lambda} \right)$$

in which X is a coordinate perpendicular to the reflecting wave front and is in the direction of propagation of the supersonic wave. Thus the integrations in (6-120) can be carried out over the volume V with the result

$$\frac{F}{VkT} = \left(\frac{\phi_1}{\omega_1} \ln \phi_1 + \frac{\phi_2}{\omega_2} \ln \phi_2 - \frac{\Omega}{2kT} \phi_1 \phi_2 \right)$$

$$+ \frac{\eta^2}{2} \left(\frac{1}{\omega_1 \phi_1} + \frac{1}{\omega_2 \phi_2} + \frac{\Omega}{kT} - 4\pi^2 \frac{H}{kT} \frac{s^2}{\lambda^2} \right) \qquad (6\text{-}121)$$

We have been taking into account the local gradients of the composition fluctuations, and the first part in (6-121) is intimately connected with Einstein's formulation. Instead of (6-121) we can write

$$\frac{F}{VkT} = \frac{F}{VkT} + \frac{1}{2} \left(\frac{\eta}{\phi_2} \right)^2 \left[\phi_2 \frac{\partial}{\partial \phi_2} \left(\frac{P^*}{kT} \right) - 4\pi^2 \phi_2^2 \frac{H}{kT} \frac{s^2}{\lambda^2} \right]$$

in which F_0 stands for the free energy of the homogeneous mixture. From (6-112) we have for unpolarized primary light,

$$\frac{I}{I_0} = 4\pi^2 \frac{V}{R^2 \lambda^4} \frac{1 + \cos^2 \theta}{2} \frac{[(C/\varkappa)(\partial \varkappa / \partial C)]^2}{C[(\partial/\partial C)(P^*/kT)]}$$

Since

$$C\left(\frac{\partial}{\partial C}\right)\left(\frac{P^*}{kT}\right) = \phi_2\left(\frac{\partial}{\partial \phi_2}\right)\left(\frac{P^*}{kT}\right)$$

the classical scattering formula can immediately be corrected for the effect of the energy connected with the existence of local gradients, by writing instead of (6-112),

$$\frac{I}{I_0} = 4\pi^2 \frac{V}{R^2 \lambda^4} \frac{1 + \cos^2\theta}{2} \frac{[(C/\varkappa)(\partial\varkappa/\partial C)]^2}{\phi_2(\partial/\partial\phi_2)(P^*/kT) - 4\pi^2\phi_2^2(H/kT)(s^2/\lambda^2)}$$

Let us now assume that an experiment is carried out with the homogeneous mixture above the critical solution temperature at a concentration which corresponds to the critical solution concentration. We know that under these circumstances,

$$\phi_2 \frac{\partial P^*}{\partial \phi_2} = \frac{kT_c}{\omega_2}(\tau - 1)$$

$$\Omega\phi_2^2 = -\frac{kT_c}{\omega_1}\left(1 + \frac{1}{x^{1/2}}\right)^2 \frac{1}{x} \frac{1}{[1 + (1/x^{1/2})]^2} = -\frac{kT_c}{\omega_2}$$

and

$$H = \frac{\Omega l^2}{6}$$

So we have to substitute for $(kT_c/\omega_2)(\tau - 1)$ the quantity

$$\frac{kT_c}{\omega_2}\left[(\tau - 1) + \frac{4\pi^2}{6}l^2 \frac{s^2}{\lambda^2}\right]$$

which gives for the scattering formula,

$$\frac{I}{I_0} = 4\pi^2 \frac{V}{R^2 \lambda^4} \frac{1 + \cos^2\theta}{2}\left(\frac{C}{\varkappa}\frac{\partial\varkappa}{\partial C}\right)^2 \frac{kT}{(kT_c/\omega_2)[(\tau - 1) + (4\pi^2/6)(l^2/\lambda^2)s^2]}$$

$$= 4\pi^2 \frac{V}{R^2 \lambda^4} \frac{1 + \cos^2\theta}{2}\left(\frac{C}{\varkappa}\frac{\partial\varkappa}{\partial C}\right)^2 \omega_2 \frac{\tau}{(\tau - 1) + (4\pi^2/6)(l^2/\lambda^2)s^2} \qquad (6\text{-}122)$$

with $\tau = T/T_c$.

The additional term in the denominator will be too small for observation whenever the critical binary mixture is far away from the critical solution temperature. However, in the vicinity of the critical point its influence increases so much that here we arrive at a dissymmetry of the scattered intensity which increases with decreasing temperature distance from that point.

Apart from a polarization factor, the intensity is proportional to

$$\int C(r) \frac{\sin ksr}{ksr} d\tau$$

with $k = 2\pi/\lambda$ [see Eq. (6-60)]. The maximum scattered intensity appears

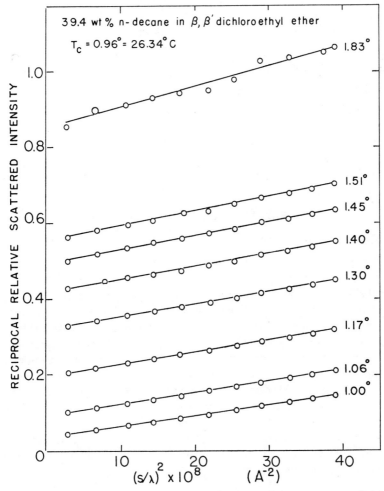

Fig. 6-14. Typical plot of reciprocal of the relative scattered intensity versus $(s/\lambda)^2$ (*33*). Temperatures of the scattering curves are expressed in relative units with $T_c = 0.96°$.

for $s = 0$, so in developing $\sin ksr$ in powers of ksr we have for small-enough angles the approximation

$$\frac{I}{I_{max}} = 1 - \frac{k^2 s^2}{6} L^2 + \cdots = 1 - \left(\frac{4\pi^2}{6}\right) L^2 \left(\frac{s^2}{\lambda^2}\right) + \cdots \qquad (6\text{-}60a)$$

if the persistence L is defined as

$$L^2 = \frac{\int r^2 C(r)\, d\tau}{\int C(r)\, d\tau}$$

On the other hand, it follows from (6-122) that

$$\frac{I}{I_{max}} = \left(1 + \frac{4\pi^2}{\tau - 1} \frac{l^2 s^2}{6\lambda^2}\right)^{-1} = 1 - \frac{4\pi^2}{6} \frac{l^2}{\lambda^2} \frac{s^2}{\tau - 1} + \cdots$$

So we come again, as in the case of critical density fluctuations to the relation

$$L^2 = \frac{l^2}{\tau - 1}$$

A typical plot of reciprocal of the relative scattered intensity versus $(s/\lambda)^2$ is shown in Fig. 6-14.

6-8. POLYMER SOLUTIONS

A. General Development

The theory developed in the preceding sections can be applied formally to polymer solutions. When one of the molecules in the fluid mixture has the form of a flexible string and therefore extends over distances large compared to the size of ordinary molecules, we may expect an additional (or enhanced) angular dissymmetry in our scattering measurements.

Let component 1 be the solvent and component 2 be the polymer. Each polymer molecule will be pictured as a flexible string of z monomers. In this section the potential-energy functions ε_{ij} refer to interactions not between the whole molecules, but between monomer segments. We shall then discuss the equivalent of the expressions Ω and H for polymer solutions.

We remark that in each polymer coil the average density of monomers can be represented by a gaussian distribution. We find for the number of monomer segments in $d\tau$,

$$\zeta\, d\tau = \frac{z}{\pi^{3/2} a^3} \exp\left(\frac{-r^2}{a^2}\right) d\tau \qquad (6\text{-}123)$$

where $d\tau$ is a volume element at a distance r from the center of gravity of the molecule. For the potential energy of one solvent molecule (kind 1) at a distance r from the center of the polymer molecule we now have

$$E_{12} = \int \varepsilon_{12} \zeta \, d\tau = \zeta W_{12} = W_{12} \left(\frac{z}{\pi^{3/2} a^3}\right) \exp\left(-\frac{r^2}{a^2}\right) \qquad (6\text{-}124)$$

provided the range of molecular forces between monomer segments can be considered small compared to the extension of the polymer. Expression (6-124) can from now on be used instead of $E_{12}(r)$ of the preceding section as a representation of the mutual energy between a solvent molecule and a polymer molecule. It remains a function of their separation distance.

In the case of two polymer molecules A and B, we indicate the distance between their centers of gravity by the letter S. The potential energy E_{22} between these two complete polymer molecules A and B then is

$$E_{22} = \int \zeta_A \zeta_B W_{22} \, d\tau = \left(\frac{z^2}{\pi^3 a^6}\right) W_{22} \int \exp\left[-\left(\frac{1}{a^2}\right)(r_A^2 + r_B^2)\right] d\tau \qquad (6\text{-}125)$$

If we let $r_A^2 = r^2$, $r_B^2 = r^2 + S^2 - 2Sr \cos\theta$, E_{22} becomes

$$E_{22} = \frac{z^2}{\pi^3 a^6} W_{22} \iint \exp\left[-\left(\frac{1}{a^2}\right)(2r^2 + S^2 - 2Sr \cos\theta)\right] 2\pi r^2 \, dr \sin\theta \, d\theta \qquad (6\text{-}126)$$

After this integration is performed, the mutual energy of two polymer molecules as a function of the distance between their centers assumes the form

$$E_{22} = W_{22} \left[\frac{1}{(2\pi)^{3/2}}\right]\left(\frac{z^2}{a^3}\right) \exp\left(-\frac{S^2}{2a^2}\right) \qquad (6\text{-}126a)$$

This expression for E_{22} can be applied to the complete molecule and can be used instead of the E_{22} of the preceding section.

If we keep this in mind and indicate the volume "occupied" by a single one of the monomer segments of the polymer string by ω_2, we have, in accordance with (6-124) and (6-126a),

$$\Omega = \frac{W_{11}}{\omega_1^2} + \frac{z^2 W_{22}}{z^2 \omega_2^2} - 2\frac{z W_{12}}{z \omega_1 \omega_2} = \frac{W_{11}}{\omega_1^2} + \frac{W_{22}}{\omega_2^2} - 2\frac{W_{22}}{\omega_1 \omega_2} \qquad (6\text{-}127)$$

since the integration of E_{12} and E_{22} over the whole space leads to the results

$$\int E_{12} \, d\tau = z W_{12} \qquad \int E_{22} \, d\tau = z^2 W_{22}$$

Using (6-124) and (6-126a) for the dependence of the mutual potential energy on the distance of the molecules, we get

$$l_{12}^2 = \frac{\int r^2 E_{12}\, d\tau}{\int E_{12}\, d\tau} = \frac{3}{2} a^2 \qquad l_{22}^2 = \frac{\int r^2 E_{22}\, d\tau}{\int E_{22}\, d\tau} = 3a^2 \qquad (6\text{-}128)$$

This gives for H the expression

$$H = \frac{1}{6}\left(\frac{W_{11}}{\omega_1^2} l_{11}^2 + \frac{W_{22}}{\omega_2^2} 3a^2 - 2\frac{W_{12}}{\omega_1 \omega_2}\frac{3}{2} a^2 \right)$$

$$\simeq \frac{a^2}{2}\left(\frac{W_{22}}{\omega_2^2} - \frac{W_{12}}{\omega_1 \omega_2} \right) \qquad (6\text{-}129)$$

if we again assume that the range of molecular forces is small compared with the size of the polymer coil. In combining the expressions (6-127) and (6-129) for Ω and H we come to the conclusion that the length l which is related to the angular dissymmetry of the scattered light in the case of polymer solutions is given by

$$l^2 = \frac{(W_{22}/\omega_2^2) - (W_{12}/\omega_1\omega_2)}{(W_{11}/\omega_1^2) + (W_{22}/\omega_2^2) - 2(W_{12}/\omega_1\omega_2)}\, 3a^2 \qquad (6\text{-}130)$$

The mean-square distance from the center of our assumed gaussian distribution of density in the polymer coil is $\frac{3}{2}a^2$. If the average square of the end-to-end distance of the chain is called R^2, it is known that the mean-square distance from the center of gravity of such a chain is $R^2/6$. We identify $R^2/6$ with $\frac{3}{2}a^2$ and so find $a^2 = R^2/9$. Thus

$$l^2 = \frac{(W_{22}/\omega_2^2) - (W_{12}/\omega_1\omega_2)}{(W_{11}/\omega_1^2) + (W_{22}/\omega_2^2) - 2(W_{12}/\omega_1\omega_2)}\, \frac{R^2}{3} \qquad (6\text{-}130a)$$

In the case of polymer solutions the dissymmetry of scattering will appear at temperature distances from the critical mixing point larger than in the case of mixtures of ordinary molecules.

B. Polydispersity of Polymers

It was found that the effect of polydispersity of polymer samples made it impossible to do the light-scattering experiments very close to the critical temperature because the high-molecular-weight fraction precipitated before the "critical solution temperature" could be reached (Table 6-1). In fact, the "critical solution temperature" is no longer precisely defined for a binary liquid mixture with a polydispersed polymer as one of

TABLE 6-1

Polystyrene in Cyclohexane (*12*)

Sample	$M_n \times 10^{-3}$	M_w/M_n	T_c, °C [a]	$T_p - T_c$, °C	$(\phi_2)_c \times 100$ [b]
A	69	1.16	19.24	0.69	6.8
B	118	1.05	21.82	0.82	5.6
C	147	1.04	23.19	0.59	5.0
D	221	1.08	24.95	0.53	4.6
E	248	1.02	25.09	0.40	4.3
F	522	1.09	27.79	0.53	2.8
G	1000	1.19	29.00	0.45	2.0
G*	(1000)		28.91	0.45	2.0

Polystyrene in Ethyl Cyclohexane (*13*)

A	69	1.16			8.2
B	118	1.05	52.79	0.34	6.6
C	147	1.04	54.66	1.11	5.8_5
D	221	1.08	57.37	0.94	5.2_5
F	522	1.09	62.02	0.93	3.6_0

[a] The second decimal place is significant only on a relative temperature scale.
[b] Expressed in volume per cent.

its two components. This is especially true when the molecular-weight distribution of the polymer is broad.

A closer examination indicates that the ratio of weight-average molecular weight M_w to number-average molecular weight M_n is a very insensitive measure of the sharpness of the molecular-weight distribution.

Suppose we assume a quadratic distribution,

$$y = A\left[1 - \left(\frac{M - M_0}{\alpha M_0}\right)^2\right]$$

in which M_0 corresponds to the molecular weight at the peak of the distribution curve. At $y = 0$,

$$(M)_{y=0} = M_0 \pm \alpha M_0 = M_0(1 \pm \alpha)$$

The total number of polymer molecules Z is

$$Z = \int y\, dM = A \int \left[1 - \left(\frac{M - M_0}{\alpha M_0}\right)^2\right] dM$$

With $x = (M - M_0)/M_0$, and consequently $M/M_0 = 1 + x$, we have

$$Z = \frac{A M_0}{\alpha^2} \int_{-\alpha}^{\alpha} (\alpha^2 - x^2) \, dx = \frac{4}{3} A M_0 \alpha$$

and

$$A = \frac{3}{4} \frac{Z}{\alpha M_0}$$

which gives

$$y = \frac{3}{4} \frac{Z}{\alpha M_0} \left[1 - \left(\frac{M - M_0}{\alpha M_0} \right)^2 \right]$$

$$M_n = \frac{\int y M \, dM}{\int y \, dM} = M_0 \frac{\int_{-\alpha}^{\alpha} [1 - (x^2/\alpha^2)](1 + x) \, dx}{\int_{-\alpha}^{\alpha} [1 - (x^2/\alpha^2)] \, dx} = M_0$$

$$M_w = \frac{\int y M^2 \, dM}{\int y M \, dM} = \frac{M_0^3 \int [1 - (x^2/\alpha^2)](1 + x)^2 \, dx}{M_0^2 \int [1 - (x^2/\alpha^2)](1 + x) \, dx}$$

$$= M_0 \frac{\int_0^{\alpha} [1 - (x^2/\alpha^2)](1 + x^2) \, dx}{\int_0^{\alpha} [1 - (x^2/\alpha^2)] \, dx} = M_0 \left(1 + \frac{1}{5} \alpha^2 \right) \qquad (6\text{-}131)$$

Thus, with a quadratic distribution curve,

$$\frac{M_w}{M_n} = 1 + \frac{\alpha^2}{5} \qquad (6\text{-}132)$$

The half-width is calculated

$$1 - \frac{x^2}{\alpha^2} = \frac{1}{2}$$

and

$$x = \frac{\alpha}{2^{1/2}}$$

C. Extension of the Polymer Coil (*28*)

In dilute solutions the extension of a polymer coil of high molecular weight can be calculated from the observed angular dissymmetry of the scattered intensity of visible light, since the light scattered at different parts of the molecule has considerable phase differences. In more concentrated solutions, the observed dissymmetry may again be used for size determinations. Near the critical mixing point, it is possible to use the angular dependence of scattered intensity to determine the range of molecular forces and the extension of the polymer coil simultaneously.

1. Application of Fluctuation Theory to Polymer Solutions

It is well known that in the case of density fluctuations in a gas Einstein's formula [Eq. (6-77)] agrees with Rayleigh's theory, which is based on particle scattering. In the case of concentration fluctuations, the scattering formula agrees only for the limiting case in which the size of the molecule is negligibly small when compared with the wavelength of visible light. Einstein's original formula [Eq. (6-74)] based on the effect of thermal fluctuations does not predict any angular dissymmetry. Then it seems important to find out the reasons for its failure when the solute molecules become bigger. Perhaps a different outlook can be developed for the interpretation of observed angular dissymmetries in more concentrated solutions from fluctuation theory.

In a liquid the local fluctuations of the refractive index (or electron density) are mainly responsible for the scattering of visible light (or X rays). For coiling macromolecules, the mass distribution of the coil may extend over distances comparable with the wavelength of visible light. Thus local fluctuations may also result from coil extensions.

We visualize each polymer molecule as a flexible chain of z monomer segments. The function $\zeta(\rho)$ represents the density of monomer segments of a single polymer chain as a function of the distance ρ from the center of gravity of the molecule. By definition

$$z = \int \zeta(\rho) \, d\tau \tag{6-133}$$

where $\zeta(\rho) \, d\tau$ is the number of monomer segments in the volume element $d\tau$, and the integration ranges over the surroundings of the molecule.

Now we want to take into account that the number of polymer molecules per cubic centimeter, n, is a variable. Following (6-84) we obtain for the total number of monomer segments per cubic centimeter, Z,

$$Z = \int n(x + \xi, y + \eta, z + \zeta)\zeta(\rho) \, d\tau \tag{6-134}$$

$$Z = n_0 z + \frac{\nabla^2 n}{6} \int \rho^2 \zeta(\rho) \, d\tau$$

$$= z\left(n_0 + \frac{r_g^2}{6}\nabla^2 n + \cdots\right) \tag{6-135}$$

where the volume element $d\tau$ ranges over the entire volume of the solution, and the average square of the radius of gyration, r_g^2, of a polymer coil can be defined

$$r_g^2 = \frac{\int \rho^2 \zeta(\rho)\, d\tau}{\int \zeta(\rho)\, d\tau}$$

The term zn_0 corresponds to the average number of monomer segments per cubic centimeter. The second term, $zr_g^2 \nabla^2 n/6$, represents deviations from the average due to extensions of the polymer coil.

The local index of refraction of a polymer solution depends on the number density of monomer segments. If the difference between the refractive index of the solvent ($\varkappa_0$) and that of the solution ($\varkappa$) is small, we may write for $\varkappa$, in terms of a series expansion of the number density of polymer molecules,

$$\varkappa = \varkappa_0 + \frac{\partial \varkappa}{\partial n} \frac{Z}{z} \tag{6-136}$$

The local fluctuations of the number density of monomer segments may be described as a superposition of waves of composition with varying directions and wavelengths. Such an interpretation of scattering (as we have previously discussed) was first introduced by Brillouin. His calculations show that, first, only those waves whose wave front can act as a mirror for the primary and scattered light, making the angle between both rays and the wave front equal and each equal to $\theta/2$, will determine the scattered intensity observed at an angle θ. Second, the wavelength Λ of those supersonic waves is related to the wavelength λ of the light by the Bragg relation:

$$\frac{1}{\Lambda} = \frac{s}{\lambda} \tag{6-75}$$

where $s = 2\sin(\theta/2)$. The component of the composition waves which meets both conditions requires that

$$v = v_0 \sin 2\pi \frac{\Lambda}{X} \tag{6-137}$$

where v represents the density fluctuation; X is perpendicular to the reflecting wave front and is in the direction of propagation of the super-sonic waves. Substituting (6-75), (6-135), and (6-137) in (6-136) we obtain

$$\varkappa = \varkappa_0 + \frac{\partial \varkappa}{\partial n} n_0 \left(1 - \frac{4\pi^2}{6} \frac{r_g^2}{\lambda^2} s^2 \right) \tag{6-138}$$

Now the term $[(C/\varkappa)(\partial\varkappa/\partial C)]^2$ which appears in Einstein's formula can be replaced by

$$\left(\frac{C}{\varkappa}\frac{\partial\varkappa}{\partial C}\right)^2\left(1-\frac{4\pi^2}{6}\frac{r_g^2}{\lambda^2}s^2\right)^2 \simeq \left(\frac{C}{\varkappa}\frac{\partial\varkappa}{\partial C}\right)^2\left(1-\frac{8\pi^2}{6}\frac{r_g^2}{\lambda^2}s^2\right)$$

The length r_g represents the persistence length of local fluctuations (due to polymer coil extensions) in the refractive index. For high-molecular-weight polymers, r_g/λ becomes large enough so that the scattered light from different parts of the inhomogeneous region has considerable phase differences. We can now extend Einstein's theory and obtain

$$\frac{I}{I_0}=\frac{4\pi^2 V}{R^2\lambda^4}\frac{[(C/\varkappa)(\partial\varkappa/\partial C)]^2[1-(8\pi^2/6)(r_g^2/\lambda^2)s^2]}{C(\partial/\partial C)(P^*/kT)} \qquad (6\text{-}139)$$

According to Debye, we find that the intensity of light scattered by a single polymer coil is proportional to (*29*)

$$i=\frac{2}{u^2}[e^{-u}-(1-u)] \qquad (6\text{-}140)$$

where $u=4\pi^2 s^2 R^2/6\lambda^2$ and R^2 is the average square of the end-to-end distance of the coil. Expanding e^{-u} in powers of u, we find that (6-140) takes on the form

$$i=1-\frac{8\pi^2}{6}\frac{r_g^2}{\lambda^2}s^2 \qquad (6\text{-}141)$$

provided that $r_g^2=R^2/6$. Terms expressing the angular dependence of scattered intensity in (6-139) and (6-141) are identical.

In a first approximation, both approaches—Rayleigh's and Einstein's—give the same scattering formula for polymer solutions of high molecular weight. However, Einstein's theory has the advantage that it is not limited to dilute solutions. A more general expression for the angular dissymmetry of scattered intensity due to the extension of polymer coils in terms of Einstein's fluctuation theory is derived in the Appendix.

2. Critical Opalescence (*27*)

The scattering formula for polymer solutions at critical solution concentrations, taking into account the extension of the polymer coil, is

$$I=\frac{C^*(T/T_c)[1-(16\pi^2/3)(r_g^2/\lambda^2)\sin^2(\theta/2)]}{(\Delta T/T_c)+(8\pi^2/3)(l^2/\lambda^2)\sin^2(\theta/2)} \qquad (6\text{-}142)$$

where I is the scattered intensity, C^* is a characteristic constant, T is the temperature in absolute units, T_c is the critical (consolute) solution temperature, $\Delta T = T - T_c$, λ is the wavelength of light in the medium, l is the molecular interaction range, θ is the scattering angle, and r_g is the radius of gyration.

Expanding the denominator in powers of s/λ, we get, for the reciprocal of the scattered intensity,

$$\frac{1}{I} \simeq \frac{T_c}{C^*T}\left[\frac{\Delta T}{T_c} + \left(\frac{2\pi^2}{3}l^2 + \frac{\Delta T}{T_c}\frac{4\pi^2}{3}r_g^2\right)\frac{s^2}{\lambda^2}\right] \qquad (6\text{-}143)$$

3. Calculation of Range of Molecular Forces and Radius of Gyration

If we are only interested in the shape of the scattering curve, it is sufficient to know the scattered intensity in relative units. However, for solutions, the measured scattered intensity in terms of galvanometer reading G has to be corrected for (1) the change in the effective scattering volume with angle, (2) the attenuation of the light beam as it travels through the light-scattering cell, and (3) the background scattering due to density fluctuations.

For cylindrical light-scattering cells, the scattered intensity, I^*, after correction for the change in the effective scattering volume, is $G \sin \theta$.

The correction for attenuation can be performed by multiplying I^* with $g(T)$; $I = I^*g(T)$, in which $g(T)$ is a function of temperature. The form of this temperature function is unimportant as long as the attenuation factor (excluding a volume correction term of $\sin \theta$ in the case of cylindrical cells) is independent of the scattering angle. We can express the experimental results by a formula of the type

$$\frac{1}{I^*} = A + B \sin^2 \frac{\theta}{2} \qquad (6\text{-}144)$$

A plot of $1/I^*$ versus $\sin^2(\theta/2)$ did indeed give straight lines as shown in Fig. 6-14. The factor $g(T)/C^*$ cancels out in the computation for T_c, l^2, and r_g^2, since only quotients of B/A or A/B enter into the calculation. Practically, it is usually unnecessary to make an attenuation correction for each I^*, except when the temperature dependence of the extrapolated zero-angle scattered intensity very near the critical point becomes of interest.

The determination of T_c is as follows: According to (6-144), we can write

$$\frac{A}{B} = \text{const. } \Delta T\left(1 + \frac{2\Delta T}{T_c}\frac{r_g^2}{l^2}\right)^{-1} \qquad (6\text{-}145)$$

or

$$\frac{A}{B} = \text{const. } \Delta T \left(1 - \frac{2\Delta T}{T_c} \frac{r_g^2}{l^2} + \cdots \right) \qquad (6\text{-}146)$$

For small ΔT, $2\Delta T r_g^2/T_c l^2$ is much less than 1, so the power series can be broken off after the first term, and (6-146) can be reduced to

$$\frac{A}{B} = \text{const. } \Delta T \qquad (6\text{-}146a)$$

where $T_c = -(\text{intercept})/(\text{slope})$ of the straight line obtained from a plot of A/B versus T.

For the computation of l^2 and r_g^2 we shall define a quantity S:

$$S = \frac{B}{A} \Delta T = \frac{8\pi^2}{3} \frac{l^2}{\lambda^2} T_c + \frac{16\pi^2}{3} \frac{r_g^2}{\lambda^2} \Delta T \qquad (6\text{-}147)$$

The behavior of S can be seen from a plot of S versus $T - T_c$:

Case 1. If l^2 and r_g^2 are independent of temperature, the curve will be linear. Slope and intercept are proportional to r_g^2/λ^2 and l^2/λ^2, respectively.

Case 2. If the curve is nonlinear, the deviations can be assigned to the temperature dependence of either r_g^2 (l^2 being constant), or l^2 (r_g^2 being constant), or both. Figure 6-15 shows a nonlinear curve from a plot of S versus $T - T_c$ for a polystyrene ($M_n = 2,820,000$) cyclohexane system from our light-scattering experiments. We know that the radius of gyration increases with temperature from dissymmetry measurements ($I_{45°}/I_{135°}$) at high temperatures, where only the extension of the polymer coil to the dissymmetry is important. In addition, experiments on the critical opalescence of polymer solutions of low molecular weights ($r_g^2/\lambda^2 \ll 1$) have shown that, at intermediate temperature distances above the critical solution temperature, l^2 is virtually independent of temperature. Therefore, the experiments indicate that in a temperature range up to 20 degrees above the critical solution temperature, only the radius of gyration changes noticeably with temperature. The range of molecular forces can be assumed to remain relatively constant within this temperature range. Then r_g^2 and l^2 can be calculated as follows:

$$r_g^2 = \frac{3\lambda^2}{16\pi^2} \frac{S - S_0}{T - T_c} \qquad (6\text{-}148)$$

$$l^2 = \frac{3\lambda^2}{8\pi^2} \frac{S_0}{T_c} \qquad (6\text{-}149)$$

where S_0 is the intercept of the S versus $T - T_c$ curve at T_c.

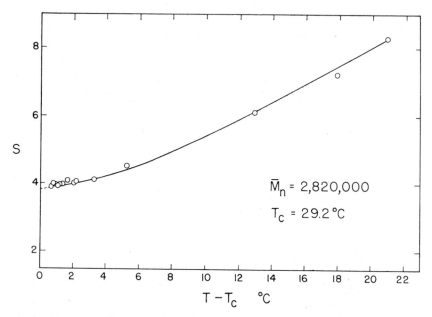

Fig. 6-15. Plot of S [defined by (6-147)] versus temperature distance from the critical temperature (*28*). Polystyrene ($\bar{M}_n = 2,820,000$) in cyclohexane.

The radius of gyration of a polymer coil in solution depends not only on the molecular weight but also on the polymer segment-solvent interaction. The polymer segment-solvent interaction increases with temperature and decreases with concentration. The more concentrated a solution is, the worse it becomes as a solvent for additional polymer. Similarly, the solvent becomes better with increasing temperature. Therefore, the radius of gyration decreases with concentration and increases with temperature.

The change of r_g with concentration can be demonstrated by measurements of the concentration dependence of the angular dissymmetry $(I^*_{45°}/I^*_{135°})$, at a temperature where the contribution of the critical opalescence to the dissymmetry is negligible. Figure 6-16 represents a plot of dissymmetry $(I^*_{45°}/I^*_{135°})$ versus concentration for a high-molecular-weight polystyrene sample. At 45°C the radius of gyration at infinite dilution has a value of 600 A, which is about 4 per cent lower than the value reported for a similar-molecular-weight polystyrene sample by Krigbaum and Carpenter ($r = 625$ A) (*30*) but is very nearly the same as that reported by Notley and Debye ($r = 602$ A) (*31*). It decreases sharply

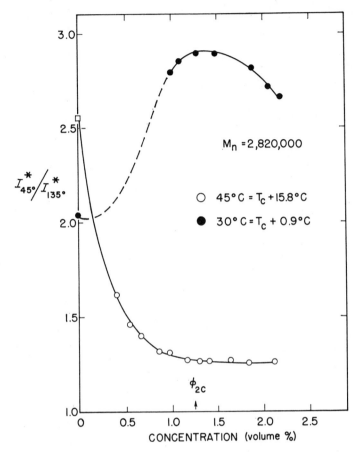

Fig. 6-16. Plot of dissymmetry $(I^*_{45°}/I^*_{135°})$ versus concentration in volume per cent (*28*). Polystyrene ($\bar{M}_n = 2,820,000$) in cyclohexane at 45°C. $\square$, value at 45°C extrapolated from a Zimm plot.

with increasing concentration and soon reaches an almost constant value of 186 A at the critical solution concentration. The radius of gyration at the critical solution concentration was calculated from (6-148) and was about three times smaller than that at infinite dilution, whereas a change in temperature does not vary the quotient of these two radii of gyration appreciably.

A plot of l^2 versus M_n for polystyrene in cyclohexane is shown in Fig.

6-17. Our measurements have revealed a striking smallness of l as compared with the radius of gyration.

The range of molecular forces for different molecular weights refers to their respective critical solution concentrations. Thus a linear relationship between l^2 and M_n is not to be expected.

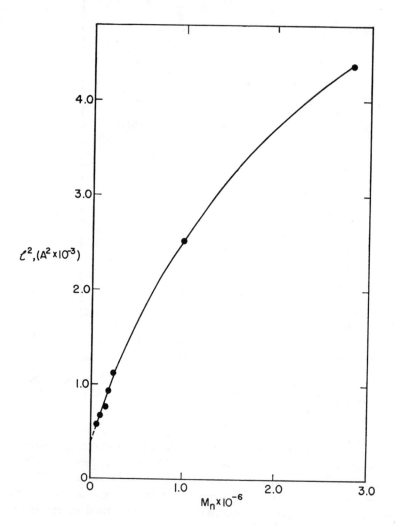

Fig. 6-17. Plot of the square of the interaction parameter l^2 as a function of molecular weight (*28*). Polystyrene in cyclohexane.

6-9. TRANSMISSION MEASUREMENTS NEAR THE CRITICAL POINT (*32*)

A. General Development

When the incident beam is polarized perpendicular to the plane of observation, the scattered intensity I, in the vicinity of the critical solution temperature, has the form

$$I = \frac{K^*(T/T_c)}{\tau - 1 + (8\pi^2/3)(l^2/\lambda^2)\sin^2(\theta/2)} \qquad K^* = K\frac{1}{\lambda^4}\left(\frac{C}{\varkappa}\frac{\partial\varkappa}{\partial C}\right)^2 \qquad (6\text{-}150)$$

in which K^* is a constant characteristic for the system, C is the critical concentration, $\varkappa$ is the refractive index of the solution, T is temperature in absolute units, T_c is the critical solution temperature, λ is the wavelength in the medium, l is the average range of molecular forces, and θ is the scattering angle.

The validity of this expression in the visible light-scattering region for polymer solutions of various molecular weights and for binary liquid mixtures of small molecules (*33, 34*) over the intermediate temperature range $(T - T_c > 0.04°)$ has definitely been established. Thus the turbidity,† α, of a binary liquid mixture at its critical solution concentration can be calculated by integrating (6-150) over all scattering angles:

$$\alpha = 2\pi K^* \int_0^\pi \frac{T/T_c}{\tau - 1 + (8\pi^2/3)(l^2/\lambda^2)\sin^2(\theta/2)}\frac{1 + \cos^2\theta}{2}\sin\theta\,d\theta \qquad (6\text{-}151)$$

Using s [$s = 2\sin(\theta/2)$] as the integration variable, we get

$$\alpha = K^*\frac{T}{T_c}\alpha_0\phi(\gamma) \tag{6-152}$$

$$\alpha_0 = \frac{8\pi}{3}\frac{1}{\tau - 1} \tag{6-152a}$$

$$\phi(\gamma) = \frac{3}{2}\left\{\frac{\ln(1 + \gamma)}{\gamma} + \frac{2}{\gamma}\left[\frac{\ln(1 + \gamma)}{\gamma} - 1\right] + \frac{2}{\gamma^2}\left[\frac{\ln(1 + \gamma)}{\gamma} - 1 + \frac{\gamma}{2}\right]\right\}$$

$$\tag{6-152b}$$

$$\gamma = \frac{8\pi^2}{3}\frac{l^2}{\lambda^2}\frac{1}{\tau - 1} \tag{6-152c}$$

† Turbidity $\equiv \alpha$, since τ has been used to represent T/T_c.

For small γ,

$$\phi(\gamma) = 1 - \frac{\gamma}{2} + \frac{7}{20}\gamma^2 - \frac{11}{40}\gamma^3 + \frac{8}{35}\gamma^4 \ldots \qquad (6\text{-}153)$$

We can experimentally make γ small enough so that the power series of $\phi(\gamma)$ can be broken off after the second term. Substituting (6-153) in (6-152), we get as an asymptotic expression for the apparent turbidity,

$$\alpha = K^* \frac{T}{T_c} \alpha_0 \left(1 - \frac{\gamma}{2}\right) \qquad (6\text{-}154)$$

The term $[(C/\varkappa)(\partial\varkappa/\partial C)]$, and consequently K^*, remain constant over a small temperature range because both $\varkappa$ and $\partial\varkappa/\partial C$ decrease with temperature. Substituting γ and α_0 from (6-152a) and (6-152c), we obtain for the reciprocal of the turbidity,

$$\frac{T}{\alpha} = \text{const.}(T - T^*) \qquad (6\text{-}155)$$

$$T^* = T_c \left(1 - \frac{8\pi^2}{6} \frac{l^2}{\lambda^2}\right) \qquad (6\text{-}155a)$$

Equations (6-155) and (6-155a) suggest that it should be possible to determine the range of molecular forces and the critical solution temperature from measurements of the wavelength dependence of the turbidity as a function of the temperature by means of turbidity measurements at the critical solution concentration.

Figure 6-18 shows a plot of the reciprocal of the extinction coefficient $1/\alpha$ against $T - T_c$ as calculated from (6-152). The values of l, T_c, and λ were chosen as $l = 30$ A, $T_c = 300°$K, λ (medium) $= 2500$ A, 3300 A.

At large temperature distances from the critical solution temperature, (6-152) can be reduced to (6-155) and $1/\alpha$ becomes a linear function of the temperature. When $T - T_c$ gets smaller, the curve bends toward the temperature axis and intercepts it at T_c. T^* corresponds to the intercept of the temperature axis extrapolated from the linear portion of the $1/\alpha$ versus $T - T_c$ curve.

The turbidity α is defined as

$$\frac{I}{I_0} = e^{-\alpha d}$$

where I and I_0 are the transmitted and the primary intensities, respectively; d is the thickness of the light path. It is apparent that α has the dimensions of reciprocal length.

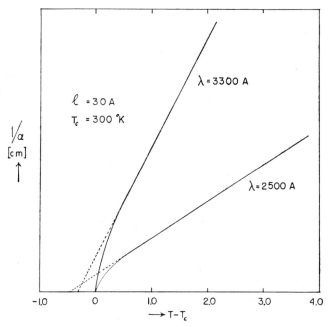

Fig. 6-18. Plot of reciprocal of the turbidity versus $T - T_c$ as calculated from (6-152) with $l = 30$ A, $T_c = 300°$K, and λ (medium) = 2500 A, 3300 A (*32*).

It follows from (6-155) that a plot of the reciprocal of the turbidity versus temperature does give a straight line at constant wavelength for polymer solutions (*32*) as well as for binary liquid mixtures (*35*), as shown typically in Fig. 6-19.

Since $T^* = T_c[1 - (8\pi^2/6)(l^2/\lambda^2)]$, l^2 and T_c can be calculated from the wavelength dependence of T^*. The value of T^* for each wavelength is given by the slope a and the intercept b of a $1/\alpha$ versus T curve; $T^* = -b/a$. A plot of the so-determined T^* versus $1/\lambda^2$ gives a straight line with slope a^* and intercept b^* as shown in Fig. 6-20. Thus

$$T_c = b^* \qquad l^2 = -\frac{6a^*}{8\pi^2 T_c}$$

T_p will coincide with T_c only in the case of a monodisperse polymer.

B. Range of Molecular Forces

The agreement with values obtained from both light scattering and turbidity measurements is indeed very good. Thus the striking smallness of l for polystyrene in cyclohexane has been confirmed.

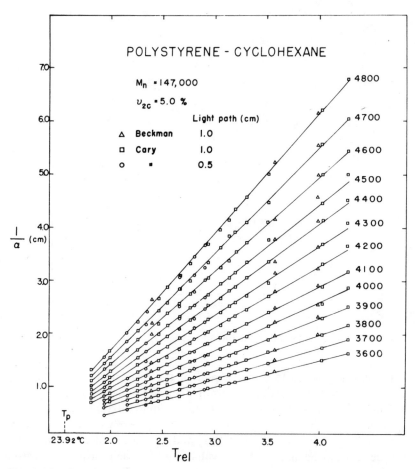

Fig. 6-19. Plot of reciprocal of the turbidity (α) versus temperature for different wavelengths. The temperature of phase separation (T_p) expressed in °C is denoted on the relative temperature scale. The wavelength in vacuum varies from 3600 to 4800 A (*32*).

The Debye interaction parameter *l* for polystyrene samples with higher molecular weights ($M_n = 552{,}000$ and $2{,}820{,}000$) is considerably smaller than the values obtained from light-scattering data. Here we shall consider the possible effect of the radius of gyration, since for higher molecular weights the extension of the polymer coil will also contribute to the turbidity. Thus we have

$$I = \frac{K^*(T/T_c)P(\theta)}{\tau - 1 + (8\pi^2/3)(l^2/\lambda^2)\sin^2(\theta/2)}$$

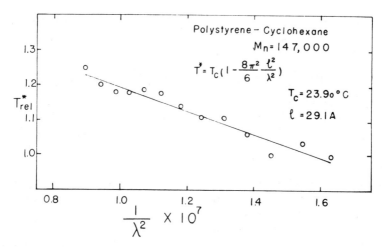

Fig. 6-20. Plot of T^* versus the reciprocal of the square of the wavelength in the medium (*32*).

in which the particle scattering factor $P(\theta) = 1 - (16\pi^2/3)(r_g^2/\lambda^2)\sin^2(\theta/2)$ $+ \cdots$. Consequently, the reciprocal of the turbidity can take the form

$$\frac{T}{\alpha} = \text{const.}(T - T^*)$$

with

$$T^* = T_c\left(1 - \frac{8\pi^2}{6}\frac{l^2}{\lambda^2}G\right) \qquad G = 1 - \frac{16}{15}\frac{r_g^2}{\lambda^2}$$

The extra term accounts for the effect of the radius of gyration. For example, the radius of gyration of a polystyrene sample with $M_n = 1 \times 10^6$ in cyclohexane at the critical solution concentration and in the neighborhood of the critical solution temperature is 133 A. If $\lambda = 3300$ A, the corresponding G is very close to 1, and the effect of the radius of gyration on turbidity measurements for low-molecular-weight polystyrene is certainly negligible. Therefore, we should re-examine the discrepancy in the Debye molecular interaction range l for high-molecular-weight polymer solutions between turbidity and light-scattering measurements with more careful experiments.

The basic assumption underlying the derivation of (6-155) is that (6-150) exactly represents the angular dissymmetry of critical opalescence in binary liquid mixtures. This has been supported by ample experimental evidence over relatively short ranges of s/λ in the visible region (*36*). Deviations of

(6-150) do seem to occur over large ranges of s/λ in the small-angle X-ray region, as we shall discuss briefly in the next section.

6-10. SMALL-ANGLE X-RAY SCATTERING

The Debye theory explaining observed dissymmetries, as set forth in previous sections (except Section 6-4), is only an approximation. In the case of density fluctuations, for instance, the density around a central molecule was represented by a development in powers of the coordinates around that molecule, and only the first terms of this development were retained. It is not necessary to use such an approximation, and we have derived a generalized interaction formula (Section 6-4) without making use of a power-series development. With the generalized equation it should be possible to obtain, from detailed measurements of the angular dependence of scattered intensity, more information on the interaction energy between two molecules as a function of their mutual separation distance. The experimental curves obtained so far from light-scattering measurements of this type have been very simple for binary liquid mixtures, e.g., polystyrene-cyclohexane, methanol-cyclohexane, carbon tetrachloride–perfluoro-methyl–cyclohexane, etc. One invariably obtains a straight line from a plot of the reciprocal intensity versus $(s/\lambda)^2$. Presumably deviations from the straight line would occur if we could make observations of the angular intensity curve close enough to the critical temperature. Unfortunately this has not been possible for polymer solutions, possibly because of the effect of polydispersity. On the other hand, light-scattering measurements show that the approximate Debye theory holds even at temperatures close to the critical solution temperature. Deviations at small values of s/λ and at small temperature distances from T_c have indeed been predicted (*37, 38*) and observed (*39*). However, measurements so near the critical point have many difficulties and should await further confirmation. In addition, several theories try to predict the scattering behavior of systems *at* the critical point. This approach, although very important in its own right, has not been emphasized here.

Instead, we want to examine the correlation curve connecting fluctuations in different points of the solution not necessarily very near the critical mixing point. Generally, the scattered intensity distribution depends on a variable of the form Ls/λ:

$$I = C^* \frac{\tau}{\tau - 1} \frac{1}{1 + (2\pi^2/3)L^2(s^2/\lambda^2)} \tag{6-156}$$

in which $L^2 = l^2/(\tau - 1)$, $\tau = T/T_c$, T is the temperature in °K, T_c is the critical temperature, C^* is a constant characteristic for the system, λ is the wavelength of light in the medium, l is the molecular interaction range, and $s = 2\sin(\theta/2)$. It is assumed that the primary light is polarized. Equation (6-156) is a good approximation; however, we may expect that the approximation breaks down if $L^2(s^2/\lambda^2)$ (not necessarily L^2 alone) becomes larger. Although (6-156) holds for small values of $L^2(s^2/\lambda^2)$ in the light-scattering range, it is likely to break down in the small-angle X-ray scattering range, where s^2/λ^2 is much bigger. Therefore, it is desirable to observe the details of the intensity curve over a large range of values of s/λ. If we use small-angle X-ray scattering we obtain a measure of shorter-range fluctuations. A composite curve constructed from experimental light scattering and small-angle X-ray scattering measurements shall increase the magnitude of accessible $L^2(s^2/\lambda^2)$ 10- to 100-fold over that obtainable with visible light alone. This indicates that our goal might be reached by using both X rays and visible light. A combination of these two techniques should enable us to probe the nature of molecular interactions in terms of fluctuations for systems near the critical point. Preliminary measurements have indeed been performed for both binary liquid mixtures (*40, 41*) and for polymer solutions (*42*).

The scattering of X rays is due mainly to the electrons dispersed in the medium, and for many practical cases these electrons can be treated as free. Under the influence of a periodic electric field, $Ee^{i\omega t}$, the amplitude x of an electron with charge e and mass m will be

$$x = -\frac{eE}{m\omega^2}e^{i\omega t} \tag{6-157}$$

The polarization P due to n such free electrons per cubic centimeter will be

$$P = -\frac{ne^2}{m\omega^2}Ee^{i\omega t} \tag{6-158}$$

which means that the dielectric constant ϵ will be

$$\epsilon = 1 - \frac{4\pi ne^2}{m\omega^2} \tag{6-159}$$

Equation (6-159) shows that the phase velocity in the medium is larger than the velocity of light in vacuum, but the dielectric constant is very close to unity. The only thing necessary to describe the X-ray scattering is to replace the dielectric constant in (6-60) by its value from (6-159). The result is

$$\frac{I}{I_0} = \left(\frac{e^2}{mc^2}\right)^2 \frac{\sin^2 \vartheta}{R^2} V \langle (\delta n)^2 \rangle \int_0^\infty C(r) \frac{\sin ksr}{ksr} d\tau \qquad (6\text{-}160)$$

The factor $(e^2/mc^2)^2$ is the scattering cross section of a single free electron; it has the value 8.06×10^{-26} cm^2. Owing to the dispersion peculiar for free electrons, the usual characteristic dependence of Rayleigh scattering on the wavelength has disappeared.

According to (6-94), we obtain for the reciprocal of the scattered intensity,

$$\frac{1}{I} \propto 1 + \frac{1}{\tau - 1}\left[\int \varepsilon(r)\left(1 - \frac{\sin Kr}{Kr}\right) d\tau \bigg/ \int \varepsilon(r)\, d\tau \right] \qquad (6\text{-}161)$$

Suppose the potential energy of interaction between two molecules follows London's attractive potential with a repulsive hard core. We may write

$$\varepsilon(r) = -\varepsilon_0 \left(\frac{d}{r}\right)^6$$

where d is the diameter of the molecule; $\varepsilon = -\varepsilon_0$ when $r = d$. Then we have (40)

$$\frac{1}{I} \propto (\tau - 1) + 1 - \frac{3}{4}\frac{\sin Kd}{Kd} - \frac{1}{4}\cos Kd + \frac{1}{8} Kd \sin Kd$$

$$+ \frac{1}{8} K^2 d^2 \cos Kd - \frac{1}{16}\pi K^3 d^3 + \frac{1}{8} K^3 d^3 \int_0^{Kd} \frac{\sin x}{x} dx$$

For small Kd

$$\frac{1}{I} \propto (\tau - 1) + \frac{1}{2} K^2 d^2 - \frac{1}{16}\pi K^3 d^3 - \frac{1}{40} K^4 d^4 + \frac{1}{5040} K^6 d^6 + \cdots$$

Thus, over large ranges of s/λ, we may expect deviations from the initial straight line in a plot of reciprocal scattered intensity versus an appropriate variable such as $(s/\lambda)^2$. In practice, the transform from observed angular dependence of scattered intensity to the potential energy of interaction as a function of their separation distance remains to be examined, especially for the case of critical binary liquid mixtures.

6-11. INELASTIC SCATTERING

Recently, the spectrum of light inelasticity scattered by either a fluid (*43*) or a binary liquid mixture (*44*) in the neighborhood of the critical point has been observed. The time-dependent correlation function should give us information on the nature of critical fluctuations, and thus on molecular interactions of systems near the critical point. However, both theories (*43, 45, 46*) and experiments are in an exploratory stage. It is logical to assume that measurements should be extended to *both* the spectral and the angular distribution of the scattered electromagnetic radiation at various fixed temperature distances from the critical point and to expect that one should find deviations from the OZD-type (Ornstein-Zernike, Debye) theory primarily in critical binary fluid mixtures rather than in one-component systems. Further developments will undoubtedly give us interesting and important information on the molecular dynamics of molecules in solution.

This monograph tries to record and to fill in the details of the Baker Lectures on Molecular Forces delivered by Professor Peter J. W. Debye. Further advances have been and will be made. In particular, I should like to call to the attention of the reader the Proceedings of the Study Week on Molecular Forces, sponsored by the Pontifical Academy of Science under the direction of Professor Peter J. W. Debye, held at Vatican City, April 1966.

APPENDIX. *Derivation of a Scattering Formula due to Polymer-Coil Extensions in Terms of Einstein's Fluctuation Theory*

According to (6-134), the total number of monomers per cubic centimeter, Z, has the form

$$Z = \int n(x + \xi, y + \eta, z + \zeta)\zeta(\rho) \, d\tau \tag{A-1}$$

To take into account the local concentration fluctuations of monomer segments due to the polymer-coil extension, we make a Fourier analysis of these fluctuations and take the component which determines the scattered intensity:

$$n = A \sin \frac{2\pi}{\Lambda} (x + \xi) \tag{A-2}$$

Substituting (A-2) in (A-1) we get

$$Z = A \int \sin \frac{2\pi}{\Lambda} (x + \xi) \zeta(\rho) \, d\tau \tag{A-3}$$

Since

$$\sin \frac{2\pi}{\Lambda} (x + \xi) = \sin \frac{2\pi}{\Lambda} x \cos \frac{2\pi}{\Lambda} \xi + \cos \frac{2\pi}{\Lambda} x \sin \frac{2\pi}{\Lambda} \xi$$

(A-3) takes the form

$$Z = A \int \left(\sin \frac{2\pi}{\Lambda} x \cos \frac{2\pi}{\Lambda} \xi + \cos \frac{2\pi}{\Lambda} x \sin \frac{2\pi}{\Lambda} \zeta \right) \zeta(\rho) \, d\tau$$

with

$$d\tau = 2\pi\rho^2 \, d\rho \sin \theta \, d\theta \quad \text{and} \quad \cos \frac{2\pi}{\Lambda} x \iint \sin \left(\frac{2\pi}{\Lambda} \rho \cos \theta \right) \sin \theta \, d\theta 2\pi\rho^2 \, d\rho = 0$$

Thus

$$Z = 2\pi A \sin \frac{2\pi}{\Lambda} x \int \rho^2 \zeta(\rho) \, d\rho \int_0^\pi \cos \left[\frac{2\pi}{\Lambda} (\rho \cos \theta) \right] \sin \theta \, d\theta$$

$$= A \sin \frac{2\pi}{\Lambda} x \int \zeta(\rho) \frac{\sin(2\pi\rho/\Lambda)}{2\pi\rho/\Lambda} \, d\tau = n_0 \int \zeta(\rho) \frac{\sin(2\pi\rho/\Lambda)}{2\pi\rho/\Lambda} \, d\tau$$

Therefore, the scattering formula contains the angular dependent factor,

$$\left[\frac{1}{z} \int \zeta(\rho) \frac{\sin(2\pi\rho/\Lambda)}{2\pi\rho/\Lambda} \, d\tau \right]^2$$

REFERENCES

1. Lord J. W. S. Rayleigh, *Phil. Mag.*, **41**, 447 (1871).
2. Lord J. W. S. Rayleigh, *Phil. Mag.*, **12**, 81 (1881).
3. A. Einstein, *Ann. Physik Chem.*, **33**, 1275 (1910).
4. P. Debye, *J. Phys. Colloid Chem.*, **51**, 18 (1947).
5. P. Debye, *J. Appl. Phys.*, **15**, 338 (1944).
6. P. M. Doty, B. H. Zimm, and H. Mark, *J. Chem. Phys.*, **12**, 144 (1944).
7. P. Debye, *J. Phys. Colloid Chem.*, **53**, 1 (1949).
8. P. Debye in *Non-Crystalline Solids* (V. D. Frechette, ed.), Wiley, New York, 1960, pp. 1–25.
9. B. H. Zimm, *J. Phys. Colloid Chem.*, **54**, 1306 (1950).
10. R. Fuerth and C. L. Williams, *Proc. Roy. Soc.* (*London*), **A224**, 104 (1954).

11. Q. Chow, *Proc. Roy. Soc. (London)*, **A224**, 100 (1954).

12. P. Debye, H. Coll, and D. Woermann, *J. Chem. Phys.*, **33**, 1746 (1960).

13. P. Debye, D. Woermann, and B. Chu, *J. Polymer Sci.*, **A1**, 255 (1963).

14. P. Debye, B. Chu, and H. Kaufmann, *J. Chem. Phys.*, **36**, 3378 (1962).

15. F. Zernike, Thesis, Amsterdam; *Arch. Neerl.*, **4**, 74 (1917).

16. F. Zernike, *Koninkl. Ned. Akad. Wetenschap. Proc.*, **17**, 793 (1916).

17. L. S. Ornstein and F. Zernike, *Physik. Z.*, **19**, 134 (1918).

18. L. S. Ornstein and F. Zernike, *Physik. Z.*, **27**, 761 (1926).

19. Y. Rocard, *J. Phys. Radium*, **4**, 165 (1933).

20. L. Brillouin, *Ann. Phys.*, **17**, 88 (1922).

21. P. Debye and F. W. Sears, *Proc. Natl. Acad. Sci. U.S.*, **18**, 409 (1932).

22. P. Debye, H. Sack, and F. Coulon, *Compt. Rend.*, **198**, 922 (1934).

23. E. H. L. Meyer and W. Ramm, *Physik. Z.*, **33**, 270 (1932).

24. W. Ramm, *Physik. Z.*, **35**, 756 (1934).

25. E. Schrödinger, *Statistical Thermodynamics*, Cambridge Univ. Press, New York, 1960, pp. 53–64.

26. P. Debye in *Electromagnetic Scattering* (M. Kerker, ed.), Macmillan, New York, 1963.

27. P. Debye, *J. Chem. Phys.*, **31**, 680 (1959).

28. P. Debye, B. Chu, and D. Woermann, *J. Chem. Phys.*, **36**, 1803 (1962).

29. P. Debye, *J. Phys. Colloid Chem.*, **51**, 18 (1947).

30. W. R. Krigbaum and D. K. Carpenter, *J. Phys. Chem.*, **59**, 1166 (1955).

31. N. T. Notley and P. Debye, *J. Polymer Sci.*, **17**, 99 (1955).

32. P. Debye, D. Woermann, and B. Chu, *J. Chem. Phys.*, **36**, 851 (1962).

33. B. Chu, *J. Chem. Phys.*, **41**, 226 (1964).

34. B. Chu and W. P. Kao, *Can. J. Chem.*, **43**, 1803 (1965).

35. B. Chu, *J. Phys. Chem.*, **67**, 1969 (1963).

36. B. Chu, *J. Am. Chem. Soc.*, **86**, 3557 (1964).

37. M. Fixman, *Advan. Chem. Phys.*, **6**, 175 (1964).

38. M. E. Fisher, *J. Math. Phys.*, **5**, 944 (1964).

39. B. Chu and W. P. Kao, *J. Chem. Phys.*, **42**, 2608 (1965).

40. P. Debye, D. Caulfield, and J. Bashaw, *J. Chem. Phys.*, **41**, 3051 (1964).

41. B. Chu, *J. Chem. Phys.*, **42**, 2293 (1965).

42. B. Chu, *J. Chem. Phys.*, **42**, 426 (1965).

43. N. C. Ford and G. Benedik, *Phys. Rev. Letters*, **15**, 649 (1965).

44. Y. Yeh, S. S. Alpert, E. Lipworth, L. Seigel, and D. Balzarini, *Bull. Am. Phys. Soc.*, **10**, 310 (1965).

45. P. Debye, *Phys. Rev. Letters*, **14**, 783 (1965).

46. R. Pecora, *J. Chem. Phys.*, **40**, 1604 (1964).

AUTHOR INDEX

Numbers in parentheses are reference numbers and indicate that an author's work is referred to although his name is not cited in the text. Numbers in italics give the page on which the complete reference is listed.

A

Abrikosova, I. I., 77, *80*
Alpert, S. S., 169 (44), *171*
Andrews, T., 7, *15*

B

Balzarini, D., 169 (44), *171*
Bashaw, J., 167 (40), 168 (40), *171*
Benedik, G., 169 (43), *171*
Benton, D. P., 77, *80*
Bergmann, P., 56 (7), *70*
Black, W., 77, *81*
Blaisse, B., 7 (4), *15*
Boltzmann, L., 43, *48*
Brillouin, L., 114, *171*

C

Carpenter, D. K., 158, *171*
Casimir, H. B. G., 71, 72, *80*
Caulfield, D., 167 (40), 168 (40), *171*
Chow, Q., 113 (11), *171*
Chu, B., 113 (13, 14), 147 (33), 151 (13), 152 (28); 158 (28), 159 (28), 160 (28), 161 (32, 33, 34), 162 (32, 35), 164 (32), 165 (32, 36), 166 (39), 167 (41, 42), *171*
Coll, H., 113 (12), 151 (12), *171*
Coulon, F., 118 (22), *171*

D

de Boer, J. H., 49, 54 (3), *70*
Debye, P., 19 (1), *26*, 34 (1), *48*, 95 (4, 5), 96 (7), 106 (8), 113 (12-14), 114, 118 (21, 22), 130 (26), 134 (27), 151 (12, 13), 152 (28), 155 (27), 158 (28), 159 (28), 160 (28), 161 (32), 163 (32), 164 (32), 165 (32), 167 (40), 168 (40), 169 (45), *170, 171*
de Jongh, J. G. V., 77 (13, 14), *81*
Derjaguin, B. V., 56 (8), *70*, 77, *80*
Dole, M., 26 (5), *27*
Doty, P. M., 96 (6), *170*

E

Einstein, A., 67, *70*, 84, 95, 119, *170*

F

Fisher, M. E., 166 (38), *171*
Fixman, M., 166 (37), *171*
Ford, N. C., 169 (43), *171*
Fowler, R. H., 26 (4), *27*
Fuerth, R., 113 (10), *170*

G

Ghosh, J. C., 26, *26*
Guggenheim, E. A., 26 (4), *27*

173

H

Hamaker, H. C., 49, *70*
Hildebrand, J. H., 14, *15*
Howe, P. G., 77, *80*
Hückel, E., 19 (1), *26*

J

Jeans, J. H., 44, *48*
Jochems, P. W. J., 77 (15), *81*

K

Kallman, H., 49, *70*
Kao, W. P., 161 (34), 166 (39), *171*
Kaufmann, H., 113 (14), *171*
Kitchener, J. A., 77, *80*
Krigbaum, W. R., 158, *171*

L

Langmuir, I., 56 (6), *70*
Lifshitz, E. M., 75, 76, *80*
Lipworth, E., 169 (44), *171*
Löw-Beer, P., 56 (7), *70*
London, F., 11, *15*, 54 (5), *70*

M

McConkey, G., 67 (12), *70*
McLone, R. R., 76, 77 (6), *80*
Mark, H., 96 (6), *170*
Meyer, E. H. L., 118 (23), *171*
Michels, A., 7, *15*
Michels, C., 7 (4), *15*

N

Notley, N. T., 158, *171*

O

Onnes, H. K., 12 (6), *15*
Ornstein, L. S., 113, *171*
Ostwald, W., 21 (2), *26*
Overbeek, J. Th. G., 49, 67 (10), *70*, 71
    (1), 77 (14), *80*

P

Partington, J. R., 3 (2), *15*
Pecora, R., 169 (46), *171*
Planck, M., 44, *48*
Polányi, M., 54 (5), *70*
Polder, D., 71, *80*
Power, E. A., 76, 77 (6), *80*
Prock, A., 67 (12), *70*
Prosser, A. P., 77, *80*
Puddington, I. E., 77, *80*

R

Ramm, W., 118 (23, 24), *171*
Rayleigh, J. W. S., Lord, 44, *48*, 83, *170*
Rocard, Y., 113, 123 (19), *171*

S

Sack, H., 118 (22), *171*
Schrödinger, E., 121 (25), *171*
Scott, R. L., 14, *15*
Sears, F. W., 114, 118 (21), *171*
Seigel, L., 169 (44), *171*
Smoluchowski, M. V., 65, *70*
Sparnaay, M. J., 77 (14, 16), 78 (16), *80*

V

van der Waals, J. D., 2, *15*
Verwey, E. J. W., 49, 67 (10), *70*, 71 (1),
    80

W

Wien, W., 46 (6), *48*
Williams, C. L., 113 (10), *170*
Willstatter, M., 49, *70*
Woermann, D., 113 (12, 13), 151 (12, 13),
    152 (28), 158 (28), 159 (28), 160 (28),
    161 (32), 163 (32), 164 (32), 165 (32),
    171

Y

Yeh, Y., 169 (44), *171*

Z

Zernike, F., 113, *171*
Zimm, B. H., 96 (6), 113 (9), *170*
Zocher, H., 56 (7), *70*

SUBJECT INDEX

A

Ampere's law, 86
Attraction
  between flat plates, 54–55, 77–80
  between flat surface and spherical particle, 52–54
  between spherical particles, 51–52
  proportional to $1/r^q$, 55–56

B

Black-body radiation, 43

C

Classical composition fluctuations, 137–141
Clustering, 17 ff.
Coagulation of colloids, 65–70
Cohesive energy density, 14–15
Colloid chemistry, molecular interaction and, 49 ff.
Colloids
  coagulation, 65–70
  London–van der Waals' attraction, 50–55
  stability, 61–65
Correlation function, 107–113
Corresponding states, law of, 8
Critical constants, 6–8

Critical opalescence, 113–130
  angular dissymmetry, 141–148
  of polymer solutions, 155–156
Critical point, 6

D

Debye-Hückel theory, 18–26
Dipole–dipole interaction, 30–31
Dipoles, 33
Double layer, 56

E

Electrolyte solution
  clustering, 18
  electrical repulsion between particles, 56–61
Electromagnetic induction, 85
Electromagnetic scattering, 83 ff.
Energy of polarization, 32 ff.

F

Faraday's law, 85
Fluctuations, 137–141
Free energy
  generalized interaction, 130–133
  of two-component system, 136

G

Gauss' law, 86–91
Generalized interaction, 130–134
Gravitation, 29–30

175

I

Ideal gas equation, 2
Index of refraction, 94–97
Induced polarization, 32
Inelastic scattering, 169
Interference, 97–101
Ionic solution, clustering, 18–26

L

Light scattering, 83 ff.
London forces, 11, 36
London's interaction theory, 71 ff.
London-van der Waals' attraction, 36–37
    colloids, 50–55

M

Maxwell-Boltzmann distribution law, 44
Maxwell's equations, 85–91
Molecules
    dynamical electrical systems, 36–42
    polarizable, 32–36
    rigid electrical systems, 30–31

O

One-component systems, 113–130

P

Particle scattering, 83–105
Planck's radiation formula, 45–48
Polarizability, 32
Polydispersity, 150–152
Polymer solutions, 148–160
    critical opalescence, 155–156
    fluctuation theory, 153–155
    polydispersity, 150–152
Polystyrene, transmission measurements,
    163–166

Potential energy
    between elementary charges, 13–14
    between molecules, 11–13
    of two-component system, 135
Poynting vector, 36

R

Radiation laws, 43–47
Radius of gyration, 101–105
Rayleigh law, 83
Rayleigh scattering, 91–94
Repulsion
    between flat plates, 52–60
    between spherical particles, 60–61

S

Scattering
    inelastic scattering, 169
    medium with irregular variation of
        dielectric constant, 105–113
    particle scattering, 83–105
    small-angle x-ray scattering, 166–168
Small-angle x-ray scattering, 166–168
Stability of colloids, 61–65
Stefan-Boltzmann law, 43

T

Transmission measurements, 161–166
Turbidity, 94–97, 161, 162
Two-component systems, 134–136

V

Van der Waals' constants, 2, 6–7
    molecular, 8–11
Van der Waals' equation, 2–3
Van der Waals' isotherms, 3–6

Z

Zero-point energy, 42–48